M000235762

Second Edition

Daily
FIELD GUIDE

A Logbook
For Home Builders

Tom Hrin

Home Builder Press
National Association of Home Builders
1201 15th Street, NW
Washington, DC 20005-2800
(800) 223-2665
www.builderbooks.com

Disclaimer

This publication is designed to provide accurate and authoritative information in regard to the subject matter covered. It is sold with the understanding that the publisher is not engaged in rendering legal, accounting, or other professional service. If legal advice or other expert assistance is required, the services of a competent professional person should be sought.

—From a Declaration of Principles jointly adopted by a Committee of the American Bar Association and a Committee of Publishers and Associations.

Daily Field Guide: A Logbook for Home Builders, Second Edition
ISBN 0-86718-516-3

© 2001 by Home Builder Press®
of the National Association of Home Builders
of the United States of America

All rights reserved. No part of this book may be reproduced or utilized in any form or by any means, electronic or mechanical, including photocopying and recording, or by any information storage and retrieval system without permission in writing from the publisher.

Cover design by David Rhodes

Digital Imagery copyright ©2001 PhotoDisc, Inc.

Printed in the United States of America

Cataloging-in-Publication data available from Library of Congress

For further information please contact:

Home Builder Press®
National Association of Home Builders
1201 15th Street, NW
Washington, DC 20005-2800
(800) 223-2665

Check us out online at **www.builderbooks.com**

Contents

A note about page numbers

Every building company develops its own preferred way of organizing and recording information. Accordingly, we have designed the *Daily Field Guide* to be flexible. You can arrange and number the pages to suit your needs and preferences. Forms that consist of more than one page are marked accordingly. If you prefer to keep the pages in their original order, use the small page numbers printed in the bottom corner of each page.

We have provided 15 sets of the Project Log and Checklists pages so that you can track 15 projects at once with the *Daily Field Guide*. New Project Log and Checklists sets begin on pages 39, 45, 51, 57, 63, 69, 75, 81, 87, 93, 99, 105, 111, 117, and 123.

About the Author

Tom Hrin is Vice President of Purchasing and a former construction manager for US HOME in northern California. Before going to work for US HOME, Mr. Hrin worked as a superintendent for Elliott Homes in Folsom, California and operated his own construction firm for a year.

Acknowledgments

The author wishes to thank Toni and Dan Gerling for their help on the prototype of the *Daily Field Guide*. He also wishes to acknowledge Francis Furtado, Vice President, Elliott Homes, and Barry Grant, Divisional Vice President, US HOME, for helping him build his career in residential construction.

Thanks also to Jeff Bryant, Folsom, California; Richard Coleman, Coleman Homes, Fredricksburg Virginia; Peyton Lumpkin, Lumpkin Construction, Montgomery, Alabama; Patrick McCourt, Barclays North, Everett, Washington; Norman Bloxham, Gulf Coast Homes, Ft. Myers, Florida; Joan Carafos, Crosstown Construction, Rochester, New York; Sue Matthews, American Homes, Inc., Ellicot City, Maryland; Dwight Morrison, BFM Home Designers & Builders, Osprey, Florida; and Jim Brooks, Jim Al Construction Corporation, Chester, New York, for their thoughtful review of this publication.

This book is produced under the general direction of Thomas M. Downs, NAHB Executive Vice President and CEO, in association with NAHB staff members Adrienne Ash, Assistant Staff Vice President, Knowledge Management; Charlotte McKamy, Publisher, Home Builder Press; John Goucher, Acquisitions Editor; David Rhodes, Art Director; and Toral Patel, Assistant Editor.

How to Use *Daily Field Guide*, Second Edition on Diskette

This diskette contains the checklists from Daily Field Guide formatted as tables in Microsoft Word 97/Windows 95. It is provided so that you can adapt the tabular checklists to suit your company's needs. The files on this diskette can only be used as word processed files on IBM compatible computers. Do not attempt to boot from this diskette.

The checklists on this diskette are in the form of Word 97/Windows 95 tabular files. More recent versions of Word, such as 98, should convert these documents into a useable format. Other word processing software (such as Ami Pro and WordPerfect) include a format conversion function. If you have word processing software other than Word, refer to your user's manual to determine how to convert these documents.

Document	Location in Book	File Name
Phone List	Page 6	Phone
Projection Chart	Page 12	Projection
Inspection Chart	Page 12	Inspection
Weekly Cleanup Schedule	Page 16	Cleanup
Weather Log	Page 22	Weather
Extra Work Performed	Page 27	Extra Work
Backcharges	Page 29	Backcharges
Equipment Rented	Page 31	Equipment
Portable Latrines	Page 33	Latrines
Vehicle Maintenance Log	Page 34	Vehicles
Warranty Literature Package	Page 38	Literature
Project Log and Checklists*	Page 39	Project Logs

These checklists are provided so that you may modify and customize them as you would any other document in Word. However, if you experience technical problems with Word, consult your user's manual.

Microsoft Word® is a registered trademarks of Microsoft Corporation.

Introduction

The construction superintendent's job is one of the most dynamic in the building industry. Superintendents must coordinate jobsite activities while dealing with architects, engineers, trade contractors, state and local governing officials, building departments, and sales representatives, as well as the builders who sign their paychecks and the homebuyers who indirectly pay their salary.

It happens to superintendents all the time. For one reason or another, a superintendent may get sidetracked and remember on the way home that he or she forgot to call in an inspection. But inspectors' phone numbers and permit numbers for houses are not always at the super's fingertips.

This *Daily Field Guide* is designed to help you, as the superintendent, not only keep the job on schedule, but also document what happens during the course of construction. If you take a few minutes at the start of each house to fill in the appropriate charts in this book, everything you need to make the job run more smoothly will be with you at all times—provided you don't lose this book.

The *Daily Field Guide* includes:

- A **Phone List** with spaces for subcontractors' office numbers, cellular phone numbers, fax machine numbers, pagers, and emergency phone numbers.
- A **Projection Chart** you can use to put together a preliminary schedule of how long you feel it will take to build a particular house in perfect conditions. This will help you project to customers and sales representatives about when a house might be ready for a walk-through.
- An **Inspection Chart** that lists the most common inspections you will need to call in to building departments.
- Basic **Conversion and Formula** data, should you need to figure and order certain materials.
- **Weekly Cleanup Schedules** so the job site stays safe and presentable.
- A **Weather Log** for tracking morning and afternoon temperatures, wind, and other elements that may affect the construction of a house and help explain why there were delays.
- **Extra Work Performed** sheets, **Backcharges** sheets, **Equipment Rented** sheets, **Portable Latrines** sheets, and a **Vehicle Maintenance Log** to help keep track of details.
- A **Warranty Literature Package** checklist that lists items that should be presented to the homeowners on the day of the walk-through.

The six-page **Project Log and Checklists**, the most important part and majority of this book, includes a list of what to order, check, and schedule when a house is released to build. It also contains daily and weekly reminders, an options and extras sheet, a material category, and more. The book is designed to track 15 houses simultaneously.

Organization is the key to any superintendent's success. Scheduling materials, trade contractors, and keeping an accurate record of jobsite activities is essential to organization. The *Daily Field Guide* is written so that whether you build three custom homes a year or a few hundred production homes, you will be able to keep track of them at a glance.

Phone List (page 1 of 4)

Date:			Project:		
Company	Company Name	Contact Person	Phone	Fax	Pager/ Mobile
Alarm company					
Appliances					
Architect					
Asphalt paving					
Building department					
Cabinets					
Cable company					
Carpet					
Ceramic tile/marble					
City/county inspection					
Closet maid (wire shelving)					
Culture marble					
Drywall					
Electric company					
Electrician					
Engineer, civil					
Engineer, structural					
Etched glass					
Excavators					
Fencing					
FHA inspection					
Final clean					
Fireplaces					
Flat concrete					
Formica					
Foundation company					
Framers					
Framing materials					
Garage cabinets					
Garage doors					
Gas company					
Graders					
Handrails					

Phone List (page 2 of 4)

Company	Company Name	Contact Person	Phone	Fax	Pager/ Mobile
Hardware					
Hardwood floors					
Hot mop					
HVAC					
Landscapers					
Lather and plasterer					
Leaded glass					
Lights					
Mason					
Mirrors					
Painting					
Phone company					
Plumbers					
Portable latrines					
Pressure wash					
Propane company					
Public works					
Rental company					
Roofers					
Rough clean					
Scaffolding					
Security company					
Shower doors					
Soil concrete test					
Steel beams/columns					
Street cleaners					
Surveyors					
Termite spray					
Trim carpenters					
Trim suppliers					
Truss company					
Tub repair					
VA inspection					
Vinyl					
Wallpaper					

Phone List (page 3 of 4)

Company	Company Name	Contact Person	Phone	Fax	Pager/ Mobile
Water department					
Waterproofing					
Weed abatement					
Window wells					
Window coverings					
Window washing					
Windows/screens					

Additional Phone Numbers

Phone List (page 4 of 4)

Non-Emergency Phone Numbers

Hospital	Hospital Location
Medical center	
Police department	
Fire department	
Sheriff department	
State police	
Ambulance	
Physician	

Employee Phone Numbers

Mechanical Subcontractor Emergency Phone Numbers

Plumbing	
Contact 2	
Contact 3	
Sewer cleanout company	
Electrical	
Contact 2	
Contact 3	
HVAC	
Contact 2	
Contact 3	
Appliance warranty and service number	

Projection Chart (page 1 of 2)

Lot #									
Permits received									
Foundation inspections									
Slabs poured									
Utilities installed									
Framers begin									
Walls stood									
Trusses/rafters									
Roof sheathing									
Windows and exterior doors installed									
Rough plumbing									
Gutters and flashing									
Roof dry-in									
Rough heat									
Mason/veneers									
Lathers									
Rough electric									
Frame inspection									
Wall insulation									
Sheetrock complete									
Garage doors									
Plastering									
Interior trim									
Interior/exterior paint									
Flat concrete									
Cabinets									
Tile/marble									
Roof complete									
HVAC trim									
Electric trim									
Graders									
Fence framing									
Landscaping									
Vinyl									
Plumbing trim									
Carpet									
Final inspection									
Final clean									
Walk-through									
Projected working days									
Actual working days									

Projection Chart (page 2 of 2)

Lot #									
Permits received									
Foundation inspections									
Slabs poured									
Utilities installed									
Framers begin									
Walls stood									
Trusses/rafters									
Roof sheathing									
Windows and exterior doors installed									
Rough plumbing									
Gutters and flashing									
Roof dry-in									
Rough heat									
Mason/veneers									
Lathers									
Rough electric									
Frame inspection									
Wall insulation									
Sheetrock complete									
Garage doors									
Plastering									
Interior trim									
Interior/exterior paint									
Flat concrete									
Cabinets									
Tile/marble									
Roof complete									
HVAC trim									
Electric trim									
Graders									
Fence framing									
Landscaping									
Vinyl									
Plumbing trim									
Carpet									
Final inspection									
Final clean									
Walk-through									
Projected working days									
Actual working days									

Inspection Chart (page 1 of 2)

Started __ / __ / __	Finished __ / __ / __	Building Dept.—Phone # _____		VA Inspector—Phone # _____			

Lot #	Address	Plan Elevation	Permit #	Ground Plumbing and Setback	Foundations			Sewer Water
					Footings	Stem Walls	Slabs	

Note: Because this chart may be used for many projects over several months, be sure to denote the year when writing in the inspection dates.

Inspection Chart (page 2 of 2)

Lot #	Tem-porary Power	Sub-floor Frame	Shear Roof Nail	Frame	Insula-tion	Shear Drywall Nail	Gas	Stucco	Final	VA Foun-dation	VA Frame	VA Final		

Note: Because this chart may be used for many projects over several months, be sure to denote the year when writing in the inspection dates.

Conversions and Formulas (page 1 of 2)

1/2	=	.500	5/16	=	.3125	1"	=	.0833
1/3	=	.333	3/8	=	.375	2"	=	.1667
2/3	=	.666	7/16	=	.4375	3"	=	.2500
1/5	=	.200	1/2	=	.500	4"	=	.3333
2/5	=	.400	9/16	=	.5625	5"	=	.4167
3/5	=	.600	5/8	=	.625	6"	=	.5000
4/5	=	.800	11/16	=	.6875	7"	=	.5833
1/16	=	.0625	3/4	=	.750	8"	=	.6667
1/8	=	.125	13/16	=	.8125	9"	=	.7500
3/16	=	.1875	7/8	=	.875	10"	=	.8333
1/4	=	.250	15/16	=	.9375	11"	=	.9167

To convert fractions of an inch to decimals of a foot multiply the fraction times 1/12.

Example:
1/16 x 1/12   or
.062 x .0833 = .00525

144 sq. in.	=	1 sq. ft. (12 x 12 = 144)
1,728 cu. in.	=	1 cu. ft. (12 x 12 x 12 = 1,728)
9 sq. ft.	=	1 sq. yd. (3 x 3 = 9)
27 cu. ft.	=	1 cu. yd. (3 x 3 x 3 = 27)
5,280 ft.	=	1 mile

43,560 sq. ft. = 1 acre
640 acres = 1 sq. mile
1 gallon of water = 8.3 pounds
π = 3.14

There are two ways to determine the number of board feet:
1. Convert all measurements to inches, then multiply the length x width x thickness and divide by 144.
   Example: 2" x 6" x 10' = 2" x 6" x 120" = 1,440   1440 / 144 = 10 board feet
   Or
2. Multiply the length (in feet) x the width x the thickness and divide by 12.
   Example: 2" x 6" x 10' = 120   120 / 12 = 10 board feet

To find the area of rectangles and squares, multiply the length by the width.

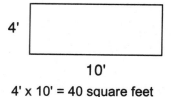

10'
4' x 10' = 40 square feet

To convert square feet to square yards, divide the number of square feet by 9. There are 9 square feet in a square yard.   40 sq. ft. / 9 = 4.4 sq. yds.

To find the amount of carpet needed in a room 17' long x 11' wide, multiply
17' x 11' = 187 sq. ft. / 9 = 20.7 sq. yds.

To find the volume of a rectangle or square, multiply the length x width x height.

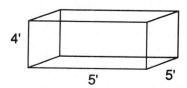

5' x 5' x 4' = 100 cubic feet

Conversions and Formulas (page 2 of 2)

To convert cubic feet into cubic yards, divide the cubic feet by 27. There are 27 cubic feet in a cubic yard.
100 cu. ft. / 27 = 3.7 cubic yards

To find the amount of concrete needed in a slab 20' long x 15' wide x 4" thick, multiply:
20' x 15' x .33' = 99 cubic feet / 27 = 3.67 cubic yards.

Note: The radius of a circle is the distance from the center point of the circle to the edge. The diameter is the distance across the circle or two times the radius.

To find the area of a circle, use the formula $R^2 \times \pi$.

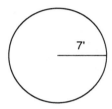

7' x 7' x 3.14 = 49' x 3.14 = 153.86

To find the volume of a cylinder, determine the area of the base and multiply by the height.

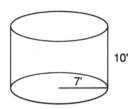

7' x 7' x 3.14 = 153.86   153.86 x 10' = 1,538.6 cu. ft.

To find the cubic yards divide by 27.   1,538.6 / 27 = 56.98 cu. yds.

Pythagorean Theorem—Formula — $A^2 + B^2 = C^2$

This theorem determines the hypotenuse (or diagonal) of a triangle, which is the angle opposite of the right or 90° angle. It can only be used on right angle triangles. This formula often is used to check the square of a house or building.

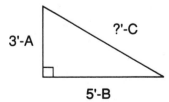

(3' x 3') + (5' x 5') = 9' + 25' = 34'

The square room of C: square root of 34' = 5.83' or 5 ft. – 10 in. is the diagonal.

Weekly Cleanup Schedule (page 1 of 6)

For the week of: _____

	Monday	Tuesday	Wednesday	Thursday	Friday
Date:					
Wood scrapped Lots cleaned					
Frame sweep completed					
Paint sweep completed					
Vinyl scrape completed					
Carpet sweep completed					
Lots cleaned for flatwork (Also order drain pipe, sleeves, and sewer boxes)					
Lots cleaned for final grading (Also locate property pins)					
Garages cleaned Walk-through					

For the week of: _____

	Monday	Tuesday	Wednesday	Thursday	Friday
Date:					
Wood scrapped Lots cleaned					
Frame sweep completed					
Paint sweep completed					
Vinyl scrape completed					
Carpet sweep completed					
Lots cleaned for flatwork (Also order drain pipe, sleeves, and sewer boxes)					
Lots cleaned for final grading (Also locate property pins)					
Garages cleaned Walk-through					

Weekly Cleanup Schedule (page 2 of 6)

For the week of: _____

	Monday	Tuesday	Wednesday	Thursday	Friday
Date:					
Wood scrapped Lots cleaned					
Frame sweep completed					
Paint sweep completed					
Vinyl scrape completed					
Carpet sweep completed					
Lots cleaned for flatwork (Also order drain pipe, sleeves, and sewer boxes)					
Lots cleaned for final grading (Also locate property pins)					
Garages cleaned Walk-through					

For the week of: _____

	Monday	Tuesday	Wednesday	Thursday	Friday
Date:					
Wood scrapped Lots cleaned					
Frame sweep completed					
Paint sweep completed					
Vinyl scrape completed					
Carpet sweep completed					
Lots cleaned for flatwork (Also order drain pipe, sleeves, and sewer boxes)					
Lots cleaned for final grading (Also locate property pins)					
Garages cleaned Walk-through					

Weekly Cleanup Schedule (page 3 of 6)

For the week of: _____

	Monday	**Tuesday**	**Wednesday**	**Thursday**	**Friday**
Date:					
Wood scrapped Lots cleaned					
Frame sweep completed					
Paint sweep completed					
Vinyl scrape completed					
Carpet sweep completed					
Lots cleaned for flatwork (Also order drain pipe, sleeves, and sewer boxes)					
Lots cleaned for final grading (Also locate property pins)					
Garages cleaned Walk-through					

For the week of: _____

	Monday	**Tuesday**	**Wednesday**	**Thursday**	**Friday**
Date:					
Wood scrapped Lots cleaned					
Frame sweep completed					
Paint sweep completed					
Vinyl scrape completed					
Carpet sweep completed					
Lots cleaned for flatwork (Also order drain pipe, sleeves, and sewer boxes)					
Lots cleaned for final grading (Also locate property pins)					
Garages cleaned Walk-through					

Weekly Cleanup Schedule (page 4 of 6)

For the week of: _____

	Monday	Tuesday	Wednesday	Thursday	Friday
Date:					
Wood scrapped Lots cleaned					
Frame sweep completed					
Paint sweep completed					
Vinyl scrape completed					
Carpet sweep completed					
Lots cleaned for flatwork (Also order drain pipe, sleeves, and sewer boxes)					
Lots cleaned for final grading (Also locate property pins)					
Garages cleaned Walk-through					

For the week of: _____

	Monday	Tuesday	Wednesday	Thursday	Friday
Date:					
Wood scrapped Lots cleaned					
Frame sweep completed					
Paint sweep completed					
Vinyl scrape completed					
Carpet sweep completed					
Lots cleaned for flatwork (Also order drain pipe, sleeves, and sewer boxes)					
Lots cleaned for final grading (Also locate property pins)					
Garages cleaned Walk-through					

Weekly Cleanup Schedule (page 5 of 6)

For the week of: _____

	Monday	Tuesday	Wednesday	Thursday	Friday
Date:					
Wood scrapped Lots cleaned					
Frame sweep completed					
Paint sweep completed					
Vinyl scrape completed					
Carpet sweep completed					
Lots cleaned for flatwork (Also order drain pipe, sleeves, and sewer boxes)					
Lots cleaned for final grading (Also locate property pins)					
Garages cleaned Walk-through					

For the week of: _____

	Monday	Tuesday	Wednesday	Thursday	Friday
Date:					
Wood scrapped Lots cleaned					
Frame sweep completed					
Paint sweep completed					
Vinyl scrape completed					
Carpet sweep completed					
Lots cleaned for flatwork (Also order drain pipe, sleeves, and sewer boxes)					
Lots cleaned for final grading (Also locate property pins)					
Garages cleaned Walk-through					

Weekly Cleanup Schedule (page 6 of 6)

For the week of: _____

	Monday	Tuesday	Wednesday	Thursday	Friday
Date:					
Wood scrapped Lots cleaned					
Frame sweep completed					
Paint sweep completed					
Vinyl scrape completed					
Carpet sweep completed					
Lots cleaned for flatwork (Also order drain pipe, sleeves, and sewer boxes)					
Lots cleaned for final grading (Also locate property pins)					
Garages cleaned Walk-through					

For the week of: _____

	Monday	Tuesday	Wednesday	Thursday	Friday
Date:					
Wood scrapped Lots cleaned					
Frame sweep completed					
Paint sweep completed					
Vinyl scrape completed					
Carpet sweep completed					
Lots cleaned for flatwork (Also order drain pipe, sleeves, and sewer boxes)					
Lots cleaned for final grading (Also locate property pins)					
Garages cleaned Walk-through					

Weather Log (page 1 of 5)

Year: _____

Date/Day	Temperature		Wind		Sky a.m.						Sky p.m.					
	a.m.	p.m.	a.m.	p.m.	Clear	Clouds	Rain	Fog	Snow	Ice	Clear	Clouds	Rain	Fog	Snow	Ice

Weather Log (page 2 of 5)

Year: _____

Date/Day	Temperature		Wind		Sky a.m.						Sky p.m.					
	a.m.	p.m.	a.m.	p.m.	Clear	Clouds	Rain	Fog	Snow	Ice	Clear	Clouds	Rain	Fog	Snow	Ice

Weather Log (page 3 of 5)

Date/Day	Temperature		Wind		Sky a.m.						Sky p.m.					
	a.m.	p.m.	a.m.	p.m.	Clear	Clouds	Rain	Fog	Snow	Ice	Clear	Clouds	Rain	Fog	Snow	Ice

Year: _____

Weather Log (page 4 of 5)

Year: _____

Date/Day	Temperature		Wind		Sky a.m.						Sky p.m.					
	a.m.	p.m.	a.m.	p.m.	Clear	Clouds	Rain	Fog	Snow	Ice	Clear	Clouds	Rain	Fog	Snow	Ice

Weather Log (page 5 of 5)

Date/Day	Temperature		Wind		Sky a.m.						Sky p.m.					
	a.m.	p.m.	a.m.	p.m.	Clear	Clouds	Rain	Fog	Snow	Ice	Clear	Clouds	Rain	Fog	Snow	Ice

Year: _____

Extra Work Performed (page 1 of 2)

Date	Lot #	Description

Extra Work Performed (page 2 of 2)

Date	Lot #	Description

Backcharges (page 1 of 2)

Date	Lot #	Description

Backcharges (page 2 of 2)

Date	Lot #	Description

Equipment Rented (page 1 of 2)

Date	Lot #	Description

Equipment Rented (page 2 of 2)

Date	Lot #	Description

Portable Latrines

Date Ordered	Unit #	Location	Date Returned

Vehicle Maintenance Log (page 1 of 2)

License Plate # _____ Year _____ Make _____

Insurance Policy # _____ Insurance Agent Phone # _____

	Date	Mileage	Service Company Name	Cost
Registration Due				
Emissions Check				
Oil Change & Lube				
Transmission Serviced				
Tune-up				
Radiator Flushed				
Brakes Checked/New				

Vehicle Maintenance Log (page 2 of 2)

	Date	Mileage	Service Company Name	Cost
New Tires				
Tires Rotated				
Lights Checked; Turn Signals; Brakes				
Wiper Blades				
Flat Tire Fixed				
Starter				
Other:				

Vehicle Maintenance Log (page 1 of 2)

License Plate # _____ Year _____ Make _____

Insurance Policy # _____ Insurance Agent Phone # _____

	Date	Mileage	Service Company Name	Cost
Registration Due				
Emissions Check				
Oil Change & Lube				
Transmission Serviced				
Tune-up				
Radiator Flushed				
Brakes Checked/New				

Vehicle Maintenance Log (page 2 of 2)

	Date	Mileage	Service Company Name	Cost
New Tires				
Tires Rotated				
Lights Checked; Turn Signals; Brakes				
Wiper Blades				
Flat Tire Fixed				
Starter				
Other:				

Warranty Literature Package

Be sure to include the following warranty documents, when applicable, in the homeowner's warranty package:

____ Building permit
____ Insulation certificate
____ Title 24 certificates—AC/furnace, water heater
____ Termite treatment certificate
____ Furnace
____ Air conditioner/condensing unit
____ Thermostat
____ Water heater
____ Range
____ Oven(s)
____ Cooktop
____ Trash compactor
____ Dishwasher
____ Microwave oven(s)
____ Range hood
____ Washer & dryer
____ Refrigerator
____ Roof material and labor
____ Landscaping information
____ Sprinkler timer/valve
____ Garage door and opener

____ Home theatre
____ Tub care
____ Faucet care
____ Garbage disposal
____ Ceiling fans
____ GFCI breakers
____ Exhaust fans
____ Smoke alarms
____ Fireplace instructions
____ Carpet warranty and care information
____ Vinyl warranty and care information
____ Hardwood floor care information
____ Window warranties
____ Vacuum warranty
____ Paint brands, color names, numbers, and locations
____ Alarm company service phone number
Mechanical subs emergency phone numbers
____ HVAC
____ Electrician
____ Plumber
____ Sewer cleanout company

Other:

_____
_____
_____
_____
_____
_____
_____
_____
_____

Project Log and Checklists (page 1 of 6)

Parcel # _____   Address _____   Lot # _____
Project # _____   Unit # _____   Phase # _____
Plan # _____   Elevation _____   Permit # _____

When a house is released to build: order, check, schedule

_____ Portable latrines _____
_____ Permit #s vs. lot #s vs. address #s _____
_____ Plot maps _____
_____ Are there storm drains in driveways? _____
_____ Sequence sheets _____
_____ Locate & mark property pins _____
_____ Locate & mark utilities _____
_____ Order bumper pipe for garage slabs _____
_____ Order mudsill (sleepers) for foundations _____
_____ Temporary power pole _____
_____ Wash out area for concrete trucks _____
_____ Retaining walls _____
_____ Steel beams _____
_____ Roof materials _____
_____ Steel columns _____
_____ Trusses _____
_____ Exterior doors & pocket door frames _____
_____ Windows _____
_____ Attic & gable vents _____
_____ Termite flashing _____
_____ Interior & exterior lights _____
_____ Exterior hardware _____
_____ Insulation for framers, plumbers, and lathers _____
_____ Drywall for framers _____
_____ Trash bins set up _____
_____ Location from Post Office where mailbox units go _____
_____ A.D.A. requirements _____

Daily/Weekly Reminders

_____ Call-in time _____
_____ Safety meetings _____
_____ Progress reports _____
_____ SWPPP reports _____
_____ Walk models _____
_____ Change model flags _____
_____ Clean dirt & mud from gutters and storm drains _____
_____ Mark electrical panels _____
_____ Mark windows _____
_____ Order fireplace chase pans _____
_____ Order tubs/showers for framers _____
_____ Temporary guard/handrails _____
_____ Order windows _____
_____ Order exterior doors & pocket door frames _____
_____ Cover thresholds _____
_____ Line sets (freon) _____
_____ Cover tubs and showers _____
_____ Garage door keys/temporary locks _____
_____ Order appliances _____
_____ Heat for vinyl/drywall _____
_____ Pipe/sleeves for flatwork _____
_____ Sewer cleanout boxes _____
_____ Retaining walls _____
_____ Mailbox pads _____
_____ Notify Post Office to set mailbox units _____
_____ Lights delivered _____
_____ Hardware delivered _____
_____ Wrought iron _____
_____ Handrails _____
_____ Leaded/etched glass _____
_____ Condensing units _____
_____ Hackouts/broken windows replaced _____
_____ Paint fireplaces/bumper pipes/cold air returns _____
_____ Floor squeaks fixed before carpet _____
_____ Concrete patched before carpet _____
_____ Roof gutters cleaned _____
_____ Utility companies—final trim _____
_____ Sidewalks repaired _____
_____ HVAC start-ups _____
_____ Return portable latrines _____

Project Log and Checklists (page 2 of 6)

Lot # _____   Address _____   Plan/Elevation _____

Options	Yes	No	Subs Notified	Extras	Yes	No	Subs Notified
Change orders received				Change orders received			
Bedroom/den/retreat				Concrete			
Fireplaces				Backyard landscaping			
2-car garage				Vacuum			
3-car garage				Plumbing			
Sewing room/shop				Electrical			
Ceiling fans				HVAC			
Bedroom lights				Alarm			
Kitchen tile				Garage door opener			
Entry tile				Window coverings			
Opaque glass				R.V. gate (extra wide)			
Microwave oven				Speaker wire			
Finish garage				Interior wall insulation			
Hardwood floors				Wallpaper			
Skylights				Gas log lighter			
Decks				Drywall bullnose corners			
Other:				Other:			

Project Log and Checklists (page 3 of 6)

Plan/Elevation _____   Lot # _____

From Homeowners, Sales Representatives, Office:		SCHD Today's Date	SCHD for	Work Complete
Siding type	Layout/chalk			
Brick type	Trench/excavate			
Stone type	FOOTING INSPECTION			
Stucco type	Forms set			
Garage door style	Sleeves/conduit			
Fireplace model #	Electrical panels			
Roof type /number	Footings poured			
Cabinet colors	STEM WALL INSPECTION			
Paint colors (interior)	Stem walls poured			
	Ground plumbing			
	Plumbing extras			
	GROUND PLUMBING/SETBACK INSPECTION			
Paint colors (exterior)	Termite spray			
	Mechanical extras			
	FOUNDATION INSPECTION			
	VA FOUNDATION INSPECTION			
	Slump/cylinder/saturation tests			
	Slab poured			
Formica selections	GARAGE SLAB INSPECTION			
Tile selections	Bumper pipes installed			
Vinyl selections	Garage slump/cylinder tests			
Carpet selections	Garage slab poured			
Pad size	Foundation waterproofed			
Appliance type	Window wells installed			
Appliance color	Foundation backfilled			
Gutter type	"As Builts" foundation			
Fence type	"As Builts" plumbing			
	TEMPORARY POWER INSPECTION			
	Utility trenches dug/barricaded			
	Trenches backfilled			
	Plumbing trench dug/barricaded			
	SEWER & WATER INSPECTION			
	Plumbing trench backfilled			
	Trenches jetted			
	Electric, phone, cable, gas			
	Plumbing			
	Schedule exterior door delivery			
	Schedule tubs/showers			

Project Log and Checklists (page 4 of 6)

Plan/Elevation _____ Lot # _____

	SCHD Today's Date	SCHD for	Work Complete		SCHD Today's Date	SCH D for	Work Complete
Schedule steel				Framing pick-up			
Framing material drop				Rough plumbing			
Layout/snap lines				Plumbing extras			
Plate				HVAC—gutters/flashing			
Girders/joists installed				Line sets—freon			
Subfloor plumbing				Fireplaces installed			
Subfloor HVAC—ducts				FIREPLACES INSPECTED			
Subfloor electrical				Felt & batt roof			
SUBFLOOR FRAME INSPECTION				Composition/shake roof installed			
Subfloor insulation				Lots scrapped			
SUBFLOOR INSULATION INSPECTION				Tubs/showers covered			
Subfloor decking				Rough HVAC—ducts			
Schedule window installation				Masonry—veneers			
Schedule fireplace installation				Insulate tubs/shear/soffits			
Schedule fireplace chase pans				Flashing for lathers			
Exterior walls framed/stood				Lathers			
Interior walls framed/stood				Hot mop			
Tubs/showers set				Stock sheetrock			
Plumb & line				Stock roof tile			
Electric meters set				Rough electric			
2nd story floor joists				Electrical extras			
Scaffold ordered 2nd story				Frame sweep			
2nd story exterior walls stood				Rough alarm wire			
2nd story interior walls stood				Rough vacuum plumbing			
Tubs/showers set				FRAME INSPECTION			
Plumb & line				VA FRAME INSPECTION			
Trusses delivered				Measure for cabinets			
Trusses installed				Drain/waste/overflow drained			
Order HVAC ducts				Re-cover tubs/showers			
Rafters installed				Wall insulation			
Roof sheathing				INSULATION INSPECTION			
Phone interface/cable box				Order interior doors			
Notify plumbers—start				Furnaces ordered			
Shear installed				Temporary heat for drywall			
ROOF/SHEAR NAIL INSPECTION				Schedule garage doors			
Scaffolding single story				Studs straightened			
Windows installed				Drywall hung			
Siding installed				DRYWALL NAIL INSPECTION			

Project Log and Checklists (page 5 of 6)

Plan/Elevation _____   Lot # _____

	SCHD Today's Date	SCHD for	Work Complete		SCHD Today's Date	SCHD for	Work Complete
GAS LINE PRESSURE INSPECTION				Schedule leaded/etched glass			
Gas meter installed				Pick & rake—graders			
Sheetrock textured				Finish grading			
Walk-through notification—sales				Fencing			
Pipe/sleeves—flatwork				Wrought iron			
Sewer boxes—driveways				Landscaping			
Fireplace faces				Heat for vinyl			
Plastering				Lino scrape			
Downspouts installed				Particle board installed			
STUCCO INSPECTION				Vinyl installed			
Exterior paint				Hardwood floors installed			
Scaffolds down				Base over vinyl/second trim			
Pick & rake flat concrete				Finish hardware			
Flat concrete poured				Bar stools installed			
Order condensing units				Closet shelves installed			
Cabinets delivered				Cabinets adjusted			
Order 1x4/plywood cabinet decking				Plumbing trim			
Kitchen sinks ordered				Appliances installed			
Interior trim				Carpet sweep			
Handrails installed				Carpet installation			
Interior paint				Window coverings installed			
Hardware delivered				Detail house			
Lights delivered				Screens installed			
Order appliances				Fireplace doors installed			
Roofers—lay tile				Gas fireplaces started up			
Cabinets installed				Sidewalks repaired			
Measure for countertops				HVAC start-up/clean furnace filter			
Tile/marble installed				HOUSE FINAL			
Extra tile				VA HOUSE FINAL			
Vanity tops				Paint touch-up			
Shower enclosures/mirrors				Final clean			
HVAC trim				Tub repair			
Formica installed				Silicon showers/tubs			
Electric trim				Garages cleaned			
Finish trim				Finish vacuum			
Windows/tubs cleaned				Garage cabinets installed			
Paint fireplaces/bumper pipe/CAR				Pressure wash concrete			
Schedule screens/fireplace doors				Walk-through			

General Notes (page 6 of 6)

Project Log and Checklists (page 1 of 6)

Parcel # _____   Address _____   Lot # _____

Project # _____   Unit # _____   Phase # _____

Plan # _____   Elevation _____   Permit # _____

**When a house is released to build:
order, check, schedule**

____ Portable latrines _____

____ Permit #s vs. lot #s vs. address #s _____

____ Plot maps _____

____ Are there storm drains in driveways? _____

____ Sequence sheets _____

____ Locate & mark property pins _____

____ Locate & mark utilities _____

____ Order bumper pipe for garage slabs _____

____ Order mudsill (sleepers) for foundations _____

____ Temporary power pole _____

____ Wash out area for concrete trucks _____

____ Retaining walls _____

____ Steel beams _____

____ Roof materials _____

____ Steel columns _____

____ Trusses _____

____ Exterior doors & pocket door frames _____

____ Windows _____

____ Attic & gable vents _____

____ Termite flashing _____

____ Interior & exterior lights _____

____ Exterior hardware _____

____ Insulation for framers, plumbers, and lathers _____

____ Drywall for framers _____

____ Trash bins set up _____

____ Location from Post Office where mailbox units go ___

____ A.D.A. requirements _____

Daily/Weekly Reminders

____ Call-in time _____

____ Safety meetings _____

____ Progress reports _____

____ SWPPP reports _____

____ Walk models _____

____ Change model flags _____

____ Clean dirt & mud from gutters and storm drains ____

____ Mark electrical panels _____

____ Mark windows _____

____ Order fireplace chase pans _____

____ Order tubs/showers for framers _____

____ Temporary guard/handrails _____

____ Order windows _____

____ Order exterior doors & pocket door frames _____

____ Cover thresholds _____

____ Line sets (freon) _____

____ Cover tubs and showers _____

____ Garage door keys/temporary locks _____

____ Order appliances _____

____ Heat for vinyl/drywall _____

____ Pipe/sleeves for flatwork _____

____ Sewer cleanout boxes _____

____ Retaining walls _____

____ Mailbox pads _____

____ Notify Post Office to set mailbox units _____

____ Lights delivered _____

____ Hardware delivered _____

____ Wrought iron _____

____ Handrails _____

____ Leaded/etched glass _____

____ Condensing units _____

____ Hackouts/broken windows replaced _____

____ Paint fireplaces/bumper pipes/cold air returns _____

____ Floor squeaks fixed before carpet _____

____ Concrete patched before carpet _____

____ Roof gutters cleaned _____

____ Utility companies—final trim _____

____ Sidewalks repaired _____

____ HVAC start-ups _____

____ Return portable latrines _____

Project Log and Checklists (page 2 of 6)

Lot # _____ **Address** _____ **Plan/Elevation** _____

Options	Yes	No	Subs Notified	Extras	Yes	No	Subs Notified
Change orders received				Change orders received			
Bedroom/den/retreat				Concrete			
Fireplaces				Backyard landscaping			
2-car garage				Vacuum			
3-car garage				Plumbing			
Sewing room/shop				Electrical			
Ceiling fans				HVAC			
Bedroom lights				Alarm			
Kitchen tile				Garage door opener			
Entry tile				Window coverings			
Opaque glass				R.V. gate (extra wide)			
Microwave oven				Speaker wire			
Finish garage				Interior wall insulation			
Hardwood floors				Wallpaper			
Skylights				Gas log lighter			
Decks				Drywall bullnose corners			
Other:				Other:			

Project Log and Checklists (page 3 of 6)

Plan/Elevation _____   Lot # _____

From Homeowners, Sales Representatives, Office:		SCHD Today's Date	SCHD for	Work Complete
Siding type	Layout/chalk			
Brick type	Trench/excavate			
Stone type	FOOTING INSPECTION			
Stucco type	Forms set			
Garage door style	Sleeves/conduit			
Fireplace model #	Electrical panels			
Roof type /number	Footings poured			
Cabinet colors	STEM WALL INSPECTION			
Paint colors (interior)	Stem walls poured			
	Ground plumbing			
	Plumbing extras			
	GROUND PLUMBING/SETBACK INSPECTION			
Paint colors (exterior)	Termite spray			
	Mechanical extras			
	FOUNDATION INSPECTION			
	VA FOUNDATION INSPECTION			
	Slump/cylinder/saturation tests			
	Slab poured			
Formica selections	GARAGE SLAB INSPECTION			
Tile selections	Bumper pipes installed			
Vinyl selections	Garage slump/cylinder tests			
Carpet selections	Garage slab poured			
Pad size	Foundation waterproofed			
Appliance type	Window wells installed			
Appliance color	Foundation backfilled			
Gutter type	"As Builts" foundation			
Fence type	"As Builts" plumbing			
	TEMPORARY POWER INSPECTION			
	Utility trenches dug/barricaded			
	Trenches backfilled			
	Plumbing trench dug/barricaded			
	SEWER & WATER INSPECTION			
	Plumbing trench backfilled			
	Trenches jetted			
	Electric, phone, cable, gas			
	Plumbing			
	Schedule exterior door delivery			
	Schedule tubs/showers			

Project Log and Checklists (page 4 of 6)

Plan/Elevation _____ Lot # _____

	SCHD Today's Date	SCHD for	Work Complete		SCHD Today's Date	SCH D for	Work Complete
Schedule steel				Framing pick-up			
Framing material drop				Rough plumbing			
Layout/snap lines				Plumbing extras			
Plate				HVAC—gutters/flashing			
Girders/joists installed				Line sets—freon			
Subfloor plumbing				Fireplaces installed			
Subfloor HVAC—ducts				FIREPLACES INSPECTED			
Subfloor electrical				Felt & batt roof			
SUBFLOOR FRAME INSPECTION				Composition/shake roof installed			
Subfloor insulation				Lots scrapped			
SUBFLOOR INSULATION INSPECTION				Tubs/showers covered			
Subfloor decking				Rough HVAC—ducts			
Schedule window installation				Masonry—veneers			
Schedule fireplace installation				Insulate tubs/shear/soffits			
Schedule fireplace chase pans				Flashing for lathers			
Exterior walls framed/stood				Lathers			
Interior walls framed/stood				Hot mop			
Tubs/showers set				Stock sheetrock			
Plumb & line				Stock roof tile			
Electric meters set				Rough electric			
2nd story floor joists				Electrical extras			
Scaffold ordered 2nd story				Frame sweep			
2nd story exterior walls stood				Rough alarm wire			
2nd story interior walls stood				Rough vacuum plumbing			
Tubs/showers set				FRAME INSPECTION			
Plumb & line				VA FRAME INSPECTION			
Trusses delivered				Measure for cabinets			
Trusses installed				Drain/waste/overflow drained			
Order HVAC ducts				Re-cover tubs/showers			
Rafters installed				Wall insulation			
Roof sheathing				INSULATION INSPECTION			
Phone interface/cable box				Order interior doors			
Notify plumbers—start				Furnaces ordered			
Shear installed				Temporary heat for drywall			
ROOF/SHEAR NAIL INSPECTION				Schedule garage doors			
Scaffolding single story				Studs straightened			
Windows installed				Drywall hung			
Siding installed				DRYWALL NAIL INSPECTION			

Project Log and Checklists (page 5 of 6)

Plan/Elevation _____   Lot # _____

	SCHD Today's Date	SCHD for	Work Complete		SCHD Today's Date	SCH D for	Work Complete
GAS LINE PRESSURE INSPECTION				Schedule leaded/etched glass			
Gas meter installed				Pick & rake—graders			
Sheetrock textured				Finish grading			
Walk-through notification—sales				Fencing			
Pipe/sleeves—flatwork				Wrought iron			
Sewer boxes—driveways				Landscaping			
Fireplace faces				Heat for vinyl			
Plastering				Lino scrape			
Downspouts installed				Particle board installed			
STUCCO INSPECTION				Vinyl installed			
Exterior paint				Hardwood floors installed			
Scaffolds down				Base over vinyl/second trim			
Pick & rake flat concrete				Finish hardware			
Flat concrete poured				Bar stools installed			
Order condensing units				Closet shelves installed			
Cabinets delivered				Cabinets adjusted			
Order 1x4/plywood cabinet decking				Plumbing trim			
Kitchen sinks ordered				Appliances installed			
Interior trim				Carpet sweep			
Handrails installed				Carpet installation			
Interior paint				Window coverings installed			
Hardware delivered				Detail house			
Lights delivered				Screens installed			
Order appliances				Fireplace doors installed			
Roofers—lay tile				Gas fireplaces started up			
Cabinets installed				Sidewalks repaired			
Measure for countertops				HVAC start-up/clean furnace filter			
Tile/marble installed				HOUSE FINAL			
Extra tile				VA HOUSE FINAL			
Vanity tops				Paint touch-up			
Shower enclosures/mirrors				Final clean			
HVAC trim				Tub repair			
Formica installed				Silicon showers/tubs			
Electric trim				Garages cleaned			
Finish trim				Finish vacuum			
Windows/tubs cleaned				Garage cabinets installed			
Paint fireplaces/bumper pipe/CAR				Pressure wash concrete			
Schedule screens/fireplace doors				Walk-through			

General Notes (page 6 of 6)

Project Log and Checklists (page 1 of 6)

Parcel # _____ Address _____ Lot # _____
Project # _____ Unit # _____ Phase # _____
Plan # _____ Elevation _____ Permit # _____

When a house is released to build: order, check, schedule

____ Portable latrines _____
____ Permit #s vs. lot #s vs. address #s _____
____ Plot maps _____
____ Are there storm drains in driveways? _____
____ Sequence sheets _____
____ Locate & mark property pins _____
____ Locate & mark utilities _____
____ Order bumper pipe for garage slabs _____
____ Order mudsill (sleepers) for foundations _____
____ Temporary power pole _____
____ Wash out area for concrete trucks _____
____ Retaining walls _____
____ Steel beams _____
____ Roof materials _____
____ Steel columns _____
____ Trusses _____
____ Exterior doors & pocket door frames _____
____ Windows _____
____ Attic & gable vents _____
____ Termite flashing _____
____ Interior & exterior lights _____
____ Exterior hardware _____
____ Insulation for framers, plumbers, and lathers ____
____ Drywall for framers _____
____ Trash bins set up _____
____ Location from Post Office where mailbox units go ____
____ A.D.A. requirements _____

Daily/Weekly Reminders

____ Call-in time _____
____ Safety meetings _____
____ Progress reports _____
____ SWPPP reports _____
____ Walk models _____
____ Change model flags _____
____ Clean dirt & mud from gutters and storm drains ____
____ Mark electrical panels _____
____ Mark windows _____
____ Order fireplace chase pans _____
____ Order tubs/showers for framers _____
____ Temporary guard/handrails _____
____ Order windows _____
____ Order exterior doors & pocket door frames ____
____ Cover thresholds _____
____ Line sets (freon) _____
____ Cover tubs and showers _____
____ Garage door keys/temporary locks _____
____ Order appliances _____
____ Heat for vinyl/drywall _____
____ Pipe/sleeves for flatwork _____
____ Sewer cleanout boxes _____
____ Retaining walls _____
____ Mailbox pads _____
____ Notify Post Office to set mailbox units _____
____ Lights delivered _____
____ Hardware delivered _____
____ Wrought iron _____
____ Handrails _____
____ Leaded/etched glass _____
____ Condensing units _____
____ Hackouts/broken windows replaced _____
____ Paint fireplaces/bumper pipes/cold air returns ____
____ Floor squeaks fixed before carpet _____
____ Concrete patched before carpet _____
____ Roof gutters cleaned _____
____ Utility companies—final trim _____
____ Sidewalks repaired _____
____ HVAC start-ups _____
____ Return portable latrines _____

Project Log and Checklists (page 2 of 6)

Lot # _____   Address _____   Plan/Elevation _____

Options	Yes	No	Subs Notified	Extras	Yes	No	Subs Notified
Change orders received				Change orders received			
Bedroom/den/retreat				Concrete			
Fireplaces				Backyard landscaping			
2-car garage				Vacuum			
3-car garage				Plumbing			
Sewing room/shop				Electrical			
Ceiling fans				HVAC			
Bedroom lights				Alarm			
Kitchen tile				Garage door opener			
Entry tile				Window coverings			
Opaque glass				R.V. gate (extra wide)			
Microwave oven				Speaker wire			
Finish garage				Interior wall insulation			
Hardwood floors				Wallpaper			
Skylights				Gas log lighter			
Decks				Drywall bullnose corners			
Other:				Other:			

Project Log and Checklists (page 3 of 6)

Plan/Elevation _____   Lot # _____

From Homeowners, Sales Representatives, Office:		SCHD Today's Date	SCHD for	Work Complete
Siding type	Layout/chalk			
Brick type	Trench/excavate			
Stone type	FOOTING INSPECTION			
Stucco type	Forms set			
Garage door style	Sleeves/conduit			
Fireplace model #	Electrical panels			
Roof type /number	Footings poured			
Cabinet colors	STEM WALL INSPECTION			
Paint colors (interior)	Stem walls poured			
	Ground plumbing			
	Plumbing extras			
	GROUND PLUMBING/SETBACK INSPECTION			
Paint colors (exterior)	Termite spray			
	Mechanical extras			
	FOUNDATION INSPECTION			
	VA FOUNDATION INSPECTION			
	Slump/cylinder/saturation tests			
	Slab poured			
Formica selections	GARAGE SLAB INSPECTION			
Tile selections	Bumper pipes installed			
Vinyl selections	Garage slump/cylinder tests			
Carpet selections	Garage slab poured			
Pad size	Foundation waterproofed			
Appliance type	Window wells installed			
Appliance color	Foundation backfilled			
Gutter type	"As Builts" foundation			
Fence type	"As Builts" plumbing			
	TEMPORARY POWER INSPECTION			
	Utility trenches dug/barricaded			
	Trenches backfilled			
	Plumbing trench dug/barricaded			
	SEWER & WATER INSPECTION			
	Plumbing trench backfilled			
	Trenches jetted			
	Electric, phone, cable, gas			
	Plumbing			
	Schedule exterior door delivery			
	Schedule tubs/showers			

Project Log and Checklists (page 4 of 6)

Plan/Elevation _____ Lot # _____

	SCHD Today's Date	SCHD for	Work Complete		SCHD Today's Date	SCHD for	Work Complete
Schedule steel				Framing pick-up			
Framing material drop				Rough plumbing			
Layout/snap lines				Plumbing extras			
Plate				HVAC—gutters/flashing			
Girders/joists installed				Line sets—freon			
Subfloor plumbing				Fireplaces installed			
Subfloor HVAC—ducts				FIREPLACES INSPECTED			
Subfloor electrical				Felt & batt roof			
SUBFLOOR FRAME INSPECTION				Composition/shake roof installed			
Subfloor insulation				Lots scrapped			
SUBFLOOR INSULATION INSPECTION				Tubs/showers covered			
Subfloor decking				Rough HVAC—ducts			
Schedule window installation				Masonry—veneers			
Schedule fireplace installation				Insulate tubs/shear/soffits			
Schedule fireplace chase pans				Flashing for lathers			
Exterior walls framed/stood				Lathers			
Interior walls framed/stood				Hot mop			
Tubs/showers set				Stock sheetrock			
Plumb & line				Stock roof tile			
Electric meters set				Rough electric			
2nd story floor joists				Electrical extras			
Scaffold ordered 2nd story				Frame sweep			
2nd story exterior walls stood				Rough alarm wire			
2nd story interior walls stood				Rough vacuum plumbing			
Tubs/showers set				FRAME INSPECTION			
Plumb & line				VA FRAME INSPECTION			
Trusses delivered				Measure for cabinets			
Trusses installed				Drain/waste/overflow drained			
Order HVAC ducts				Re-cover tubs/showers			
Rafters installed				Wall insulation			
Roof sheathing				INSULATION INSPECTION			
Phone interface/cable box				Order interior doors			
Notify plumbers—start				Furnaces ordered			
Shear installed				Temporary heat for drywall			
ROOF/SHEAR NAIL INSPECTION				Schedule garage doors			
Scaffolding single story				Studs straightened			
Windows installed				Drywall hung			
Siding installed				DRYWALL NAIL INSPECTION			

Project Log and Checklists (page 5 of 6)

Plan/Elevation _____   Lot # _____

	SCHD Today's Date	SCHD for	Work Complete		SCHD Today's Date	SCHD for	Work Complete
GAS LINE PRESSURE INSPECTION				Schedule leaded/etched glass			
Gas meter installed				Pick & rake—graders			
Sheetrock textured				Finish grading			
Walk-through notification—sales				Fencing			
Pipe/sleeves—flatwork				Wrought iron			
Sewer boxes—driveways				Landscaping			
Fireplace faces				Heat for vinyl			
Plastering				Lino scrape			
Downspouts installed				Particle board installed			
STUCCO INSPECTION				Vinyl installed			
Exterior paint				Hardwood floors installed			
Scaffolds down				Base over vinyl/second trim			
Pick & rake flat concrete				Finish hardware			
Flat concrete poured				Bar stools installed			
Order condensing units				Closet shelves installed			
Cabinets delivered				Cabinets adjusted			
Order 1x4/plywood cabinet decking				Plumbing trim			
Kitchen sinks ordered				Appliances installed			
Interior trim				Carpet sweep			
Handrails installed				Carpet installation			
Interior paint				Window coverings installed			
Hardware delivered				Detail house			
Lights delivered				Screens installed			
Order appliances				Fireplace doors installed			
Roofers—lay tile				Gas fireplaces started up			
Cabinets installed				Sidewalks repaired			
Measure for countertops				HVAC start-up/clean furnace filter			
Tile/marble installed				HOUSE FINAL			
Extra tile				VA HOUSE FINAL			
Vanity tops				Paint touch-up			
Shower enclosures/mirrors				Final clean			
HVAC trim				Tub repair			
Formica installed				Silicon showers/tubs			
Electric trim				Garages cleaned			
Finish trim				Finish vacuum			
Windows/tubs cleaned				Garage cabinets installed			
Paint fireplaces/bumper pipe/CAR				Pressure wash concrete			
Schedule screens/fireplace doors				Walk-through			

General Notes (page 6 of 6)

Project Log and Checklists (page 1 of 6)

Parcel # _____   Address _____   Lot # _____
Project # _____   Unit # _____   Phase # _____
Plan # _____   Elevation _____   Permit # _____

When a house is released to build: order, check, schedule

- ____ Portable latrines _____
- ____ Permit #s vs. lot #s vs. address #s _____
- ____ Plot maps _____
- ____ Are there storm drains in driveways? _____
- ____ Sequence sheets _____
- ____ Locate & mark property pins _____
- ____ Locate & mark utilities _____
- ____ Order bumper pipe for garage slabs _____
- ____ Order mudsill (sleepers) for foundations _____
- ____ Temporary power pole _____
- ____ Wash out area for concrete trucks _____
- ____ Retaining walls _____
- ____ Steel beams _____
- ____ Roof materials _____
- ____ Steel columns _____
- ____ Trusses _____
- ____ Exterior doors & pocket door frames _____
- ____ Windows _____
- ____ Attic & gable vents _____
- ____ Termite flashing _____
- ____ Interior & exterior lights _____
- ____ Exterior hardware _____
- ____ Insulation for framers, plumbers, and lathers ____
- ____ Drywall for framers _____
- ____ Trash bins set up _____
- ____ Location from Post Office where mailbox units go __
- ____ A.D.A. requirements _____

Daily/Weekly Reminders

- ____ Call-in time _____
- ____ Safety meetings _____
- ____ Progress reports _____
- ____ SWPPP reports _____
- ____ Walk models _____
- ____ Change model flags _____
- ____ Clean dirt & mud from gutters and storm drains ____
- ____ Mark electrical panels _____
- ____ Mark windows _____
- ____ Order fireplace chase pans _____
- ____ Order tubs/showers for framers _____
- ____ Temporary guard/handrails _____
- ____ Order windows _____
- ____ Order exterior doors & pocket door frames _____
- ____ Cover thresholds _____
- ____ Line sets (freon) _____
- ____ Cover tubs and showers _____
- ____ Garage door keys/temporary locks _____
- ____ Order appliances _____
- ____ Heat for vinyl/drywall _____
- ____ Pipe/sleeves for flatwork _____
- ____ Sewer cleanout boxes _____
- ____ Retaining walls _____
- ____ Mailbox pads _____
- ____ Notify Post Office to set mailbox units _____
- ____ Lights delivered _____
- ____ Hardware delivered _____
- ____ Wrought iron _____
- ____ Handrails _____
- ____ Leaded/etched glass _____
- ____ Condensing units _____
- ____ Hackouts/broken windows replaced _____
- ____ Paint fireplaces/bumper pipes/cold air returns _____
- ____ Floor squeaks fixed before carpet _____
- ____ Concrete patched before carpet _____
- ____ Roof gutters cleaned _____
- ____ Utility companies—final trim _____
- ____ Sidewalks repaired _____
- ____ HVAC start-ups _____
- ____ Return portable latrines _____

Project Log and Checklists (page 2 of 6)

Lot # _____   Address _____   Plan/Elevation _____

Options	Yes	No	Subs Notified	Extras	Yes	No	Subs Notified
Change orders received				Change orders received			
Bedroom/den/retreat				Concrete			
Fireplaces				Backyard landscaping			
2-car garage				Vacuum			
3-car garage				Plumbing			
Sewing room/shop				Electrical			
Ceiling fans				HVAC			
Bedroom lights				Alarm			
Kitchen tile				Garage door opener			
Entry tile				Window coverings			
Opaque glass				R.V. gate (extra wide)			
Microwave oven				Speaker wire			
Finish garage				Interior wall insulation			
Hardwood floors				Wallpaper			
Skylights				Gas log lighter			
Decks				Drywall bullnose corners			
Other:				Other:			

Project Log and Checklists (page 3 of 6)

Plan/Elevation _____ Lot # _____

From Homeowners, Sales Representatives, Office:		SCHD Today's Date	SCHD for	Work Complete
Siding type	Layout/chalk			
Brick type	Trench/excavate			
Stone type	FOOTING INSPECTION			
Stucco type	Forms set			
Garage door style	Sleeves/conduit			
Fireplace model #	Electrical panels			
Roof type /number	Footings poured			
Cabinet colors	STEM WALL INSPECTION			
Paint colors (interior)	Stem walls poured			
	Ground plumbing			
	Plumbing extras			
	GROUND PLUMBING/SETBACK INSPECTION			
Paint colors (exterior)	Termite spray			
	Mechanical extras			
	FOUNDATION INSPECTION			
	VA FOUNDATION INSPECTION			
	Slump/cylinder/saturation tests			
	Slab poured			
Formica selections	GARAGE SLAB INSPECTION			
Tile selections	Bumper pipes installed			
Vinyl selections	Garage slump/cylinder tests			
Carpet selections	Garage slab poured			
Pad size	Foundation waterproofed			
Appliance type	Window wells installed			
Appliance color	Foundation backfilled			
Gutter type	"As Builts" foundation			
Fence type	"As Builts" plumbing			
	TEMPORARY POWER INSPECTION			
	Utility trenches dug/barricaded			
	Trenches backfilled			
	Plumbing trench dug/barricaded			
	SEWER & WATER INSPECTION			
	Plumbing trench backfilled			
	Trenches jetted			
	Electric, phone, cable, gas			
	Plumbing			
	Schedule exterior door delivery			
	Schedule tubs/showers			

Project Log and Checklists (page 4 of 6)

Plan/Elevation _____ Lot # _____

	SCHD Today's Date	SCH D for	Work Complete		SCHD Today's Date	SCH D for	Work Complete
Schedule steel				Framing pick-up			
Framing material drop				Rough plumbing			
Layout/snap lines				Plumbing extras			
Plate				HVAC—gutters/flashing			
Girders/joists installed				Line sets—freon			
Subfloor plumbing				Fireplaces installed			
Subfloor HVAC—ducts				FIREPLACES INSPECTED			
Subfloor electrical				Felt & batt roof			
SUBFLOOR FRAME INSPECTION				Composition/shake roof installed			
Subfloor insulation				Lots scrapped			
SUBFLOOR INSULATION INSPECTION				Tubs/showers covered			
Subfloor decking				Rough HVAC—ducts			
Schedule window installation				Masonry—veneers			
Schedule fireplace installation				Insulate tubs/shear/soffits			
Schedule fireplace chase pans				Flashing for lathers			
Exterior walls framed/stood				Lathers			
Interior walls framed/stood				Hot mop			
Tubs/showers set				Stock sheetrock			
Plumb & line				Stock roof tile			
Electric meters set				Rough electric			
2nd story floor joists				Electrical extras			
Scaffold ordered 2nd story				Frame sweep			
2nd story exterior walls stood				Rough alarm wire			
2nd story interior walls stood				Rough vacuum plumbing			
Tubs/showers set				FRAME INSPECTION			
Plumb & line				VA FRAME INSPECTION			
Trusses delivered				Measure for cabinets			
Trusses installed				Drain/waste/overflow drained			
Order HVAC ducts				Re-cover tubs/showers			
Rafters installed				Wall insulation			
Roof sheathing				INSULATION INSPECTION			
Phone interface/cable box				Order interior doors			
Notify plumbers—start				Furnaces ordered			
Shear installed				Temporary heat for drywall			
ROOF/SHEAR NAIL INSPECTION				Schedule garage doors			
Scaffolding single story				Studs straightened			
Windows installed				Drywall hung			
Siding installed				DRYWALL NAIL INSPECTION			

Project Log and Checklists (page 5 of 6)

Plan/Elevation _____ Lot # _____

	SCHD Today's Date	SCHD for	Work Complete		SCHD Today's Date	SCH D for	Work Complete
GAS LINE PRESSURE INSPECTION				Schedule leaded/etched glass			
Gas meter installed				Pick & rake—graders			
Sheetrock textured				Finish grading			
Walk-through notification—sales				Fencing			
Pipe/sleeves—flatwork				Wrought iron			
Sewer boxes—driveways				Landscaping			
Fireplace faces				Heat for vinyl			
Plastering				Lino scrape			
Downspouts installed				Particle board installed			
STUCCO INSPECTION				Vinyl installed			
Exterior paint				Hardwood floors installed			
Scaffolds down				Base over vinyl/second trim			
Pick & rake flat concrete				Finish hardware			
Flat concrete poured				Bar stools installed			
Order condensing units				Closet shelves installed			
Cabinets delivered				Cabinets adjusted			
Order 1x4/plywood cabinet decking				Plumbing trim			
Kitchen sinks ordered				Appliances installed			
Interior trim				Carpet sweep			
Handrails installed				Carpet installation			
Interior paint				Window coverings installed			
Hardware delivered				Detail house			
Lights delivered				Screens installed			
Order appliances				Fireplace doors installed			
Roofers—lay tile				Gas fireplaces started up			
Cabinets installed				Sidewalks repaired			
Measure for countertops				HVAC start-up/clean furnace filter			
Tile/marble installed				HOUSE FINAL			
Extra tile				VA HOUSE FINAL			
Vanity tops				Paint touch-up			
Shower enclosures/mirrors				Final clean			
HVAC trim				Tub repair			
Formica installed				Silicon showers/tubs			
Electric trim				Garages cleaned			
Finish trim				Finish vacuum			
Windows/tubs cleaned				Garage cabinets installed			
Paint fireplaces/bumper pipe/CAR				Pressure wash concrete			
Schedule screens/fireplace doors				Walk-through			

General Notes (page 6 of 6)

Project Log and Checklists (page 1 of 6)

Parcel # _____ Address _____ Lot # _____
Project # _____ Unit # _____ Phase # _____
Plan # _____ Elevation _____ Permit # _____

When a house is released to build:
order, check, schedule

_____ Portable latrines _____
_____ Permit #s vs. lot #s vs. address #s _____
_____ Plot maps _____
_____ Are there storm drains in driveways? _____
_____ Sequence sheets _____
_____ Locate & mark property pins _____
_____ Locate & mark utilities _____
_____ Order bumper pipe for garage slabs _____
_____ Order mudsill (sleepers) for foundations _____
_____ Temporary power pole _____
_____ Wash out area for concrete trucks _____
_____ Retaining walls _____
_____ Steel beams _____
_____ Roof materials _____
_____ Steel columns _____
_____ Trusses _____
_____ Exterior doors & pocket door frames _____
_____ Windows _____
_____ Attic & gable vents _____
_____ Termite flashing _____
_____ Interior & exterior lights _____
_____ Exterior hardware _____
_____ Insulation for framers, plumbers, and lathers _____
_____ Drywall for framers _____
_____ Trash bins set up _____
_____ Location from Post Office where mailbox units go ___
_____ A.D.A. requirements _____

Daily/Weekly Reminders

_____ Call-in time _____
_____ Safety meetings _____
_____ Progress reports _____
_____ SWPPP reports _____
_____ Walk models _____
_____ Change model flags _____
_____ Clean dirt & mud from gutters and storm drains _____
_____ Mark electrical panels _____
_____ Mark windows _____
_____ Order fireplace chase pans _____
_____ Order tubs/showers for framers _____
_____ Temporary guard/handrails _____
_____ Order windows _____
_____ Order exterior doors & pocket door frames _____
_____ Cover thresholds _____
_____ Line sets (freon) _____
_____ Cover tubs and showers _____
_____ Garage door keys/temporary locks _____
_____ Order appliances _____
_____ Heat for vinyl/drywall _____
_____ Pipe/sleeves for flatwork _____
_____ Sewer cleanout boxes _____
_____ Retaining walls _____
_____ Mailbox pads _____
_____ Notify Post Office to set mailbox units _____
_____ Lights delivered _____
_____ Hardware delivered _____
_____ Wrought iron _____
_____ Handrails _____
_____ Leaded/etched glass _____
_____ Condensing units _____
_____ Hackouts/broken windows replaced _____
_____ Paint fireplaces/bumper pipes/cold air returns _____
_____ Floor squeaks fixed before carpet _____
_____ Concrete patched before carpet _____
_____ Roof gutters cleaned _____
_____ Utility companies—final trim _____
_____ Sidewalks repaired _____
_____ HVAC start-ups _____
_____ Return portable latrines _____

Project Log and Checklists (page 2 of 6)

Lot # _____   Address _____   Plan/Elevation _____

Options	Yes	No	Subs Notified	Extras	Yes	No	Subs Notified
Change orders received				Change orders received			
Bedroom/den/retreat				Concrete			
Fireplaces				Backyard landscaping			
2-car garage				Vacuum			
3-car garage				Plumbing			
Sewing room/shop				Electrical			
Ceiling fans				HVAC			
Bedroom lights				Alarm			
Kitchen tile				Garage door opener			
Entry tile				Window coverings			
Opaque glass				R.V. gate (extra wide)			
Microwave oven				Speaker wire			
Finish garage				Interior wall insulation			
Hardwood floors				Wallpaper			
Skylights				Gas log lighter			
Decks				Drywall bullnose corners			
Other:				Other:			

Project Log and Checklists (page 3 of 6)

Plan/Elevation _____ Lot # _____

From Homeowners, Sales Representatives, Office:		SCHD Today's Date	SCHD for	Work Complete
Siding type	Layout/chalk			
Brick type	Trench/excavate			
Stone type	FOOTING INSPECTION			
Stucco type	Forms set			
Garage door style	Sleeves/conduit			
Fireplace model #	Electrical panels			
Roof type /number	Footings poured			
Cabinet colors	STEM WALL INSPECTION			
Paint colors (interior)	Stem walls poured			
	Ground plumbing			
	Plumbing extras			
	GROUND PLUMBING/SETBACK INSPECTION			
Paint colors (exterior)	Termite spray			
	Mechanical extras			
	FOUNDATION INSPECTION			
	VA FOUNDATION INSPECTION			
	Slump/cylinder/saturation tests			
	Slab poured			
Formica selections	GARAGE SLAB INSPECTION			
Tile selections	Bumper pipes installed			
Vinyl selections	Garage slump/cylinder tests			
Carpet selections	Garage slab poured			
Pad size	Foundation waterproofed			
Appliance type	Window wells installed			
Appliance color	Foundation backfilled			
Gutter type	"As Builts" foundation			
Fence type	"As Builts" plumbing			
	TEMPORARY POWER INSPECTION			
	Utility trenches dug/barricaded			
	Trenches backfilled			
	Plumbing trench dug/barricaded			
	SEWER & WATER INSPECTION			
	Plumbing trench backfilled			
	Trenches jetted			
	Electric, phone, cable, gas			
	Plumbing			
	Schedule exterior door delivery			
	Schedule tubs/showers			

Project Log and Checklists (page 4 of 6)

Plan/Elevation _____ Lot # _____

	SCHD Today's Date	SCHD for	Work Complete		SCHD Today's Date	SCH D for	Work Complete
Schedule steel				Framing pick-up			
Framing material drop				Rough plumbing			
Layout/snap lines				Plumbing extras			
Plate				HVAC—gutters/flashing			
Girders/joists installed				Line sets—freon			
Subfloor plumbing				Fireplaces installed			
Subfloor HVAC—ducts				FIREPLACES INSPECTED			
Subfloor electrical				Felt & batt roof			
SUBFLOOR FRAME INSPECTION				Composition/shake roof installed			
Subfloor insulation				Lots scrapped			
SUBFLOOR INSULATION INSPECTION				Tubs/showers covered			
Subfloor decking				Rough HVAC—ducts			
Schedule window installation				Masonry—veneers			
Schedule fireplace installation				Insulate tubs/shear/soffits			
Schedule fireplace chase pans				Flashing for lathers			
Exterior walls framed/stood				Lathers			
Interior walls framed/stood				Hot mop			
Tubs/showers set				Stock sheetrock			
Plumb & line				Stock roof tile			
Electric meters set				Rough electric			
2nd story floor joists				Electrical extras			
Scaffold ordered 2nd story				Frame sweep			
2nd story exterior walls stood				Rough alarm wire			
2nd story interior walls stood				Rough vacuum plumbing			
Tubs/showers set				FRAME INSPECTION			
Plumb & line				VA FRAME INSPECTION			
Trusses delivered				Measure for cabinets			
Trusses installed				Drain/waste/overflow drained			
Order HVAC ducts				Re-cover tubs/showers			
Rafters installed				Wall insulation			
Roof sheathing				INSULATION INSPECTION			
Phone interface/cable box				Order interior doors			
Notify plumbers—start				Furnaces ordered			
Shear installed				Temporary heat for drywall			
ROOF/SHEAR NAIL INSPECTION				Schedule garage doors			
Scaffolding single story				Studs straightened			
Windows installed				Drywall hung			
Siding installed				DRYWALL NAIL INSPECTION			

Project Log and Checklists (page 5 of 6)

Plan/Elevation _____   Lot # _____

	SCHD Today's Date	SCHD for	Work Complete		SCHD Today's Date	SCHD for	Work Complete
GAS LINE PRESSURE INSPECTION				Schedule leaded/etched glass			
Gas meter installed				Pick & rake—graders			
Sheetrock textured				Finish grading			
Walk-through notification—sales				Fencing			
Pipe/sleeves—flatwork				Wrought iron			
Sewer boxes—driveways				Landscaping			
Fireplace faces				Heat for vinyl			
Plastering				Lino scrape			
Downspouts installed				Particle board installed			
STUCCO INSPECTION				Vinyl installed			
Exterior paint				Hardwood floors installed			
Scaffolds down				Base over vinyl/second trim			
Pick & rake flat concrete				Finish hardware			
Flat concrete poured				Bar stools installed			
Order condensing units				Closet shelves installed			
Cabinets delivered				Cabinets adjusted			
Order 1x4/plywood cabinet decking				Plumbing trim			
Kitchen sinks ordered				Appliances installed			
Interior trim				Carpet sweep			
Handrails installed				Carpet installation			
Interior paint				Window coverings installed			
Hardware delivered				Detail house			
Lights delivered				Screens installed			
Order appliances				Fireplace doors installed			
Roofers—lay tile				Gas fireplaces started up			
Cabinets installed				Sidewalks repaired			
Measure for countertops				HVAC start-up/clean furnace filter			
Tile/marble installed				HOUSE FINAL			
Extra tile				VA HOUSE FINAL			
Vanity tops				Paint touch-up			
Shower enclosures/mirrors				Final clean			
HVAC trim				Tub repair			
Formica installed				Silicon showers/tubs			
Electric trim				Garages cleaned			
Finish trim				Finish vacuum			
Windows/tubs cleaned				Garage cabinets installed			
Paint fireplaces/bumper pipe/CAR				Pressure wash concrete			
Schedule screens/fireplace doors				Walk-through			

General Notes (page 6 of 6)

Project Log and Checklists (page 1 of 6)

Parcel # _____ Address _____ Lot # _____
Project # _____ Unit # _____ Phase # _____
Plan # _____ Elevation _____ Permit # _____

**When a house is released to build:
order, check, schedule**

- ____ Portable latrines _____
- ____ Permit #s vs. lot #s vs. address #s _____
- ____ Plot maps _____
- ____ Are there storm drains in driveways? _____
- ____ Sequence sheets _____
- ____ Locate & mark property pins _____
- ____ Locate & mark utilities _____
- ____ Order bumper pipe for garage slabs _____
- ____ Order mudsill (sleepers) for foundations _____
- ____ Temporary power pole _____
- ____ Wash out area for concrete trucks _____
- ____ Retaining walls _____
- ____ Steel beams _____
- ____ Roof materials _____
- ____ Steel columns _____
- ____ Trusses _____
- ____ Exterior doors & pocket door frames _____
- ____ Windows _____
- ____ Attic & gable vents _____
- ____ Termite flashing _____
- ____ Interior & exterior lights _____
- ____ Exterior hardware _____
- ____ Insulation for framers, plumbers, and lathers _____
- ____ Drywall for framers _____
- ____ Trash bins set up _____
- ____ Location from Post Office where mailbox units go ___
- ____ A.D.A. requirements _____

Daily/Weekly Reminders

- ____ Call-in time _____
- ____ Safety meetings _____
- ____ Progress reports _____
- ____ SWPPP reports _____
- ____ Walk models _____
- ____ Change model flags _____
- ____ Clean dirt & mud from gutters and storm drains ____
- ____ Mark electrical panels _____
- ____ Mark windows _____
- ____ Order fireplace chase pans _____
- ____ Order tubs/showers for framers _____
- ____ Temporary guard/handrails _____
- ____ Order windows _____
- ____ Order exterior doors & pocket door frames _____
- ____ Cover thresholds _____
- ____ Line sets (freon) _____
- ____ Cover tubs and showers _____
- ____ Garage door keys/temporary locks _____
- ____ Order appliances _____
- ____ Heat for vinyl/drywall _____
- ____ Pipe/sleeves for flatwork _____
- ____ Sewer cleanout boxes _____
- ____ Retaining walls _____
- ____ Mailbox pads _____
- ____ Notify Post Office to set mailbox units _____
- ____ Lights delivered _____
- ____ Hardware delivered _____
- ____ Wrought iron _____
- ____ Handrails _____
- ____ Leaded/etched glass _____
- ____ Condensing units _____
- ____ Hackouts/broken windows replaced _____
- ____ Paint fireplaces/bumper pipes/cold air returns _____
- ____ Floor squeaks fixed before carpet _____
- ____ Concrete patched before carpet _____
- ____ Roof gutters cleaned _____
- ____ Utility companies—final trim _____
- ____ Sidewalks repaired _____
- ____ HVAC start-ups _____
- ____ Return portable latrines _____

Project Log and Checklists (page 2 of 6)

Lot # _____ Address _____ Plan/Elevation _____

Options	Yes	No	Subs Notified	Extras	Yes	No	Subs Notified
Change orders received				Change orders received			
Bedroom/den/retreat				Concrete			
Fireplaces				Backyard landscaping			
2-car garage				Vacuum			
3-car garage				Plumbing			
Sewing room/shop				Electrical			
Ceiling fans				HVAC			
Bedroom lights				Alarm			
Kitchen tile				Garage door opener			
Entry tile				Window coverings			
Opaque glass				R.V. gate (extra wide)			
Microwave oven				Speaker wire			
Finish garage				Interior wall insulation			
Hardwood floors				Wallpaper			
Skylights				Gas log lighter			
Decks				Drywall bullnose corners			
Other:				Other:			

Project Log and Checklists (page 3 of 6)

Plan/Elevation _____   Lot # _____

From Homeowners, Sales Representatives, Office:		SCHD Today's Date	SCHD for	Work Complete
Siding type	Layout/chalk			
Brick type	Trench/excavate			
Stone type	FOOTING INSPECTION			
Stucco type	Forms set			
Garage door style	Sleeves/conduit			
Fireplace model #	Electrical panels			
Roof type /number	Footings poured			
Cabinet colors	STEM WALL INSPECTION			
Paint colors (interior)	Stem walls poured			
	Ground plumbing			
	Plumbing extras			
	GROUND PLUMBING/SETBACK INSPECTION			
Paint colors (exterior)	Termite spray			
	Mechanical extras			
	FOUNDATION INSPECTION			
	VA FOUNDATION INSPECTION			
	Slump/cylinder/saturation tests			
	Slab poured			
Formica selections	GARAGE SLAB INSPECTION			
Tile selections	Bumper pipes installed			
Vinyl selections	Garage slump/cylinder tests			
Carpet selections	Garage slab poured			
Pad size	Foundation waterproofed			
Appliance type	Window wells installed			
Appliance color	Foundation backfilled			
Gutter type	"As Builts" foundation			
Fence type	"As Builts" plumbing			
	TEMPORARY POWER INSPECTION			
	Utility trenches dug/barricaded			
	Trenches backfilled			
	Plumbing trench dug/barricaded			
	SEWER & WATER INSPECTION			
	Plumbing trench backfilled			
	Trenches jetted			
	Electric, phone, cable, gas			
	Plumbing			
	Schedule exterior door delivery			
	Schedule tubs/showers			

Project Log and Checklists (page 4 of 6)

Plan/Elevation _____ Lot # _____

	SCHD Today's Date	SCHD for	Work Complete		SCHD Today's Date	SCH D for	Work Complete
Schedule steel				Framing pick-up			
Framing material drop				Rough plumbing			
Layout/snap lines				Plumbing extras			
Plate				HVAC—gutters/flashing			
Girders/joists installed				Line sets—freon			
Subfloor plumbing				Fireplaces installed			
Subfloor HVAC—ducts				FIREPLACES INSPECTED			
Subfloor electrical				Felt & batt roof			
SUBFLOOR FRAME INSPECTION				Composition/shake roof installed			
Subfloor insulation				Lots scrapped			
SUBFLOOR INSULATION INSPECTION				Tubs/showers covered			
Subfloor decking				Rough HVAC—ducts			
Schedule window installation				Masonry—veneers			
Schedule fireplace installation				Insulate tubs/shear/soffits			
Schedule fireplace chase pans				Flashing for lathers			
Exterior walls framed/stood				Lathers			
Interior walls framed/stood				Hot mop			
Tubs/showers set				Stock sheetrock			
Plumb & line				Stock roof tile			
Electric meters set				Rough electric			
2nd story floor joists				Electrical extras			
Scaffold ordered 2nd story				Frame sweep			
2nd story exterior walls stood				Rough alarm wire			
2nd story interior walls stood				Rough vacuum plumbing			
Tubs/showers set				FRAME INSPECTION			
Plumb & line				VA FRAME INSPECTION			
Trusses delivered				Measure for cabinets			
Trusses installed				Drain/waste/overflow drained			
Order HVAC ducts				Re-cover tubs/showers			
Rafters installed				Wall insulation			
Roof sheathing				INSULATION INSPECTION			
Phone interface/cable box				Order interior doors			
Notify plumbers—start				Furnaces ordered			
Shear installed				Temporary heat for drywall			
ROOF/SHEAR NAIL INSPECTION				Schedule garage doors			
Scaffolding single story				Studs straightened			
Windows installed				Drywall hung			
Siding installed				DRYWALL NAIL INSPECTION			

Project Log and Checklists (page 5 of 6)

Plan/Elevation _____   Lot # _____

	SCHD Today's Date	SCHD for	Work Complete		SCHD Today's Date	SCHD for	Work Complete
GAS LINE PRESSURE INSPECTION				Schedule leaded/etched glass			
Gas meter installed				Pick & rake—graders			
Sheetrock textured				Finish grading			
Walk-through notification—sales				Fencing			
Pipe/sleeves—flatwork				Wrought iron			
Sewer boxes—driveways				Landscaping			
Fireplace faces				Heat for vinyl			
Plastering				Lino scrape			
Downspouts installed				Particle board installed			
STUCCO INSPECTION				Vinyl installed			
Exterior paint				Hardwood floors installed			
Scaffolds down				Base over vinyl/second trim			
Pick & rake flat concrete				Finish hardware			
Flat concrete poured				Bar stools installed			
Order condensing units				Closet shelves installed			
Cabinets delivered				Cabinets adjusted			
Order 1x4/plywood cabinet decking				Plumbing trim			
Kitchen sinks ordered				Appliances installed			
Interior trim				Carpet sweep			
Handrails installed				Carpet installation			
Interior paint				Window coverings installed			
Hardware delivered				Detail house			
Lights delivered				Screens installed			
Order appliances				Fireplace doors installed			
Roofers—lay tile				Gas fireplaces started up			
Cabinets installed				Sidewalks repaired			
Measure for countertops				HVAC start-up/clean furnace filter			
Tile/marble installed				HOUSE FINAL			
Extra tile				VA HOUSE FINAL			
Vanity tops				Paint touch-up			
Shower enclosures/mirrors				Final clean			
HVAC trim				Tub repair			
Formica installed				Silicon showers/tubs			
Electric trim				Garages cleaned			
Finish trim				Finish vacuum			
Windows/tubs cleaned				Garage cabinets installed			
Paint fireplaces/bumper pipe/CAR				Pressure wash concrete			
Schedule screens/fireplace doors				Walk-through			

General Notes (page 6 of 6)

Project Log and Checklists (page 1 of 6)

Parcel # _____ Address _____ Lot # _____
Project # _____ Unit # _____ Phase # _____
Plan # _____ Elevation _____ Permit # _____

When a house is released to build:
order, check, schedule

_____ Portable latrines _____
_____ Permit #s vs. lot #s vs. address #s _____
_____ Plot maps _____
_____ Are there storm drains in driveways? _____
_____ Sequence sheets _____
_____ Locate & mark property pins _____
_____ Locate & mark utilities _____
_____ Order bumper pipe for garage slabs _____
_____ Order mudsill (sleepers) for foundations _____
_____ Temporary power pole _____
_____ Wash out area for concrete trucks _____
_____ Retaining walls _____
_____ Steel beams _____
_____ Roof materials _____
_____ Steel columns _____
_____ Trusses _____
_____ Exterior doors & pocket door frames _____
_____ Windows _____
_____ Attic & gable vents _____
_____ Termite flashing _____
_____ Interior & exterior lights _____
_____ Exterior hardware _____
_____ Insulation for framers, plumbers, and lathers _____
_____ Drywall for framers _____
_____ Trash bins set up _____
_____ Location from Post Office where mailbox units go ___
_____ A.D.A. requirements _____

Daily/Weekly Reminders

_____ Call-in time _____
_____ Safety meetings _____
_____ Progress reports _____
_____ SWPPP reports _____
_____ Walk models _____
_____ Change model flags _____
_____ Clean dirt & mud from gutters and storm drains _____
_____ Mark electrical panels _____
_____ Mark windows _____
_____ Order fireplace chase pans _____
_____ Order tubs/showers for framers _____
_____ Temporary guard/handrails _____
_____ Order windows _____
_____ Order exterior doors & pocket door frames _____
_____ Cover thresholds _____
_____ Line sets (freon) _____
_____ Cover tubs and showers _____
_____ Garage door keys/temporary locks _____
_____ Order appliances _____
_____ Heat for vinyl/drywall _____
_____ Pipe/sleeves for flatwork _____
_____ Sewer cleanout boxes _____
_____ Retaining walls _____
_____ Mailbox pads _____
_____ Notify Post Office to set mailbox units _____
_____ Lights delivered _____
_____ Hardware delivered _____
_____ Wrought iron _____
_____ Handrails _____
_____ Leaded/etched glass _____
_____ Condensing units _____
_____ Hackouts/broken windows replaced _____
_____ Paint fireplaces/bumper pipes/cold air returns _____
_____ Floor squeaks fixed before carpet _____
_____ Concrete patched before carpet _____
_____ Roof gutters cleaned _____
_____ Utility companies—final trim _____
_____ Sidewalks repaired _____
_____ HVAC start-ups _____
_____ Return portable latrines _____

Project Log and Checklists (page 2 of 6)

Lot # _____   **Address** _____   **Plan/Elevation** _____

Options	Yes	No	Subs Notified	Extras	Yes	No	Subs Notified
Change orders received				Change orders received			
Bedroom/den/retreat				Concrete			
Fireplaces				Backyard landscaping			
2-car garage				Vacuum			
3-car garage				Plumbing			
Sewing room/shop				Electrical			
Ceiling fans				HVAC			
Bedroom lights				Alarm			
Kitchen tile				Garage door opener			
Entry tile				Window coverings			
Opaque glass				R.V. gate (extra wide)			
Microwave oven				Speaker wire			
Finish garage				Interior wall insulation			
Hardwood floors				Wallpaper			
Skylights				Gas log lighter			
Decks				Drywall bullnose corners			
Other:				Other:			

Project Log and Checklists (page 3 of 6)

Plan/Elevation _____   Lot # _____

From Homeowners, Sales Representatives, Office:		SCHD Today's Date	SCHD for	Work Complete
Siding type	Layout/chalk			
Brick type	Trench/excavate			
Stone type	FOOTING INSPECTION			
Stucco type	Forms set			
Garage door style	Sleeves/conduit			
Fireplace model #	Electrical panels			
Roof type /number	Footings poured			
Cabinet colors	STEM WALL INSPECTION			
Paint colors (interior)	Stem walls poured			
	Ground plumbing			
	Plumbing extras			
	GROUND PLUMBING/SETBACK INSPECTION			
Paint colors (exterior)	Termite spray			
	Mechanical extras			
	FOUNDATION INSPECTION			
	VA FOUNDATION INSPECTION			
	Slump/cylinder/saturation tests			
	Slab poured			
Formica selections	GARAGE SLAB INSPECTION			
Tile selections	Bumper pipes installed			
Vinyl selections	Garage slump/cylinder tests			
Carpet selections	Garage slab poured			
Pad size	Foundation waterproofed			
Appliance type	Window wells installed			
Appliance color	Foundation backfilled			
Gutter type	"As Builts" foundation			
Fence type	"As Builts" plumbing			
	TEMPORARY POWER INSPECTION			
	Utility trenches dug/barricaded			
	Trenches backfilled			
	Plumbing trench dug/barricaded			
	SEWER & WATER INSPECTION			
	Plumbing trench backfilled			
	Trenches jetted			
	Electric, phone, cable, gas			
	Plumbing			
	Schedule exterior door delivery			
	Schedule tubs/showers			

Project Log and Checklists (page 4 of 6)

Plan/Elevation _____   Lot # _____

	SCHD Today's Date	SCHD for	Work Complete		SCHD Today's Date	SCHD for	Work Complete
Schedule steel				Framing pick-up			
Framing material drop				Rough plumbing			
Layout/snap lines				Plumbing extras			
Plate				HVAC—gutters/flashing			
Girders/joists installed				Line sets—freon			
Subfloor plumbing				Fireplaces installed			
Subfloor HVAC—ducts				FIREPLACES INSPECTED			
Subfloor electrical				Felt & batt roof			
SUBFLOOR FRAME INSPECTION				Composition/shake roof installed			
Subfloor insulation				Lots scrapped			
SUBFLOOR INSULATION INSPECTION				Tubs/showers covered			
Subfloor decking				Rough HVAC—ducts			
Schedule window installation				Masonry—veneers			
Schedule fireplace installation				Insulate tubs/shear/soffits			
Schedule fireplace chase pans				Flashing for lathers			
Exterior walls framed/stood				Lathers			
Interior walls framed/stood				Hot mop			
Tubs/showers set				Stock sheetrock			
Plumb & line				Stock roof tile			
Electric meters set				Rough electric			
2nd story floor joists				Electrical extras			
Scaffold ordered 2nd story				Frame sweep			
2nd story exterior walls stood				Rough alarm wire			
2nd story interior walls stood				Rough vacuum plumbing			
Tubs/showers set				FRAME INSPECTION			
Plumb & line				VA FRAME INSPECTION			
Trusses delivered				Measure for cabinets			
Trusses installed				Drain/waste/overflow drained			
Order HVAC ducts				Re-cover tubs/showers			
Rafters installed				Wall insulation			
Roof sheathing				INSULATION INSPECTION			
Phone interface/cable box				Order interior doors			
Notify plumbers—start				Furnaces ordered			
Shear installed				Temporary heat for drywall			
ROOF/SHEAR NAIL INSPECTION				Schedule garage doors			
Scaffolding single story				Studs straightened			
Windows installed				Drywall hung			
Siding installed				DRYWALL NAIL INSPECTION			

Project Log and Checklists (page 5 of 6)

Plan/Elevation _____   Lot # _____

	SCHD Today's Date	SCHD for	Work Complete		SCHD Today's Date	SCH D for	Work Complete
GAS LINE PRESSURE INSPECTION				Schedule leaded/etched glass			
Gas meter installed				Pick & rake—graders			
Sheetrock textured				Finish grading			
Walk-through notification—sales				Fencing			
Pipe/sleeves—flatwork				Wrought iron			
Sewer boxes—driveways				Landscaping			
Fireplace faces				Heat for vinyl			
Plastering				Lino scrape			
Downspouts installed				Particle board installed			
STUCCO INSPECTION				Vinyl installed			
Exterior paint				Hardwood floors installed			
Scaffolds down				Base over vinyl/second trim			
Pick & rake flat concrete				Finish hardware			
Flat concrete poured				Bar stools installed			
Order condensing units				Closet shelves installed			
Cabinets delivered				Cabinets adjusted			
Order 1x4/plywood cabinet decking				Plumbing trim			
Kitchen sinks ordered				Appliances installed			
Interior trim				Carpet sweep			
Handrails installed				Carpet installation			
Interior paint				Window coverings installed			
Hardware delivered				Detail house			
Lights delivered				Screens installed			
Order appliances				Fireplace doors installed			
Roofers—lay tile				Gas fireplaces started up			
Cabinets installed				Sidewalks repaired			
Measure for countertops				HVAC start-up/clean furnace filter			
Tile/marble installed				HOUSE FINAL			
Extra tile				VA HOUSE FINAL			
Vanity tops				Paint touch-up			
Shower enclosures/mirrors				Final clean			
HVAC trim				Tub repair			
Formica installed				Silicon showers/tubs			
Electric trim				Garages cleaned			
Finish trim				Finish vacuum			
Windows/tubs cleaned				Garage cabinets installed			
Paint fireplaces/bumper pipe/CAR				Pressure wash concrete			
Schedule screens/fireplace doors				Walk-through			

General Notes (page 6 of 6)

Project Log and Checklists (page 1 of 6)

Parcel # _____ Address _____ Lot # _____

Project # _____ Unit # _____ Phase # _____

Plan # _____ Elevation _____ Permit # _____

**When a house is released to build:
order, check, schedule**

___ Portable latrines _____

___ Permit #s vs. lot #s vs. address #s _____

___ Plot maps _____

___ Are there storm drains in driveways? _____

___ Sequence sheets _____

___ Locate & mark property pins _____

___ Locate & mark utilities _____

___ Order bumper pipe for garage slabs _____

___ Order mudsill (sleepers) for foundations _____

___ Temporary power pole _____

___ Wash out area for concrete trucks _____

___ Retaining walls _____

___ Steel beams _____

___ Roof materials _____

___ Steel columns _____

___ Trusses _____

___ Exterior doors & pocket door frames _____

___ Windows _____

___ Attic & gable vents _____

___ Termite flashing _____

___ Interior & exterior lights _____

___ Exterior hardware _____

___ Insulation for framers, plumbers, and lathers _____

___ Drywall for framers _____

___ Trash bins set up _____

___ Location from Post Office where mailbox units go ___

___ A.D.A. requirements _____

Daily/Weekly Reminders

___ Call-in time _____

___ Safety meetings _____

___ Progress reports _____

___ SWPPP reports _____

___ Walk models _____

___ Change model flags _____

___ Clean dirt & mud from gutters and storm drains ___

___ Mark electrical panels _____

___ Mark windows _____

___ Order fireplace chase pans _____

___ Order tubs/showers for framers _____

___ Temporary guard/handrails _____

___ Order windows _____

___ Order exterior doors & pocket door frames _____

___ Cover thresholds _____

___ Line sets (freon) _____

___ Cover tubs and showers _____

___ Garage door keys/temporary locks _____

___ Order appliances _____

___ Heat for vinyl/drywall _____

___ Pipe/sleeves for flatwork _____

___ Sewer cleanout boxes _____

___ Retaining walls _____

___ Mailbox pads _____

___ Notify Post Office to set mailbox units _____

___ Lights delivered _____

___ Hardware delivered _____

___ Wrought iron _____

___ Handrails _____

___ Leaded/etched glass _____

___ Condensing units _____

___ Hackouts/broken windows replaced _____

___ Paint fireplaces/bumper pipes/cold air returns _____

___ Floor squeaks fixed before carpet _____

___ Concrete patched before carpet _____

___ Roof gutters cleaned _____

___ Utility companies—final trim _____

___ Sidewalks repaired _____

___ HVAC start-ups _____

___ Return portable latrines _____

Project Log and Checklists (page 2 of 6)

Lot # _____   **Address** _____   **Plan/Elevation** _____

Options	Yes	No	Subs Notified	Extras	Yes	No	Subs Notified
Change orders received				Change orders received			
Bedroom/den/retreat				Concrete			
Fireplaces				Backyard landscaping			
2-car garage				Vacuum			
3-car garage				Plumbing			
Sewing room/shop				Electrical			
Ceiling fans				HVAC			
Bedroom lights				Alarm			
Kitchen tile				Garage door opener			
Entry tile				Window coverings			
Opaque glass				R.V. gate (extra wide)			
Microwave oven				Speaker wire			
Finish garage				Interior wall insulation			
Hardwood floors				Wallpaper			
Skylights				Gas log lighter			
Decks				Drywall bullnose corners			
Other:				Other:			

Project Log and Checklists (page 3 of 6)

Plan/Elevation _____   Lot # _____

From Homeowners, Sales Representatives, Office:		SCHD Today's Date	SCHD for	Work Complete
Siding type	Layout/chalk			
Brick type	Trench/excavate			
Stone type	FOOTING INSPECTION			
Stucco type	Forms set			
Garage door style	Sleeves/conduit			
Fireplace model #	Electrical panels			
Roof type /number	Footings poured			
Cabinet colors	STEM WALL INSPECTION			
Paint colors (interior)	Stem walls poured			
	Ground plumbing			
	Plumbing extras			
	GROUND PLUMBING/SETBACK INSPECTION			
Paint colors (exterior)	Termite spray			
	Mechanical extras			
	FOUNDATION INSPECTION			
	VA FOUNDATION INSPECTION			
	Slump/cylinder/saturation tests			
	Slab poured			
Formica selections	GARAGE SLAB INSPECTION			
Tile selections	Bumper pipes installed			
Vinyl selections	Garage slump/cylinder tests			
Carpet selections	Garage slab poured			
Pad size	Foundation waterproofed			
Appliance type	Window wells installed			
Appliance color	Foundation backfilled			
Gutter type	"As Builts" foundation			
Fence type	"As Builts" plumbing			
	TEMPORARY POWER INSPECTION			
	Utility trenches dug/barricaded			
	Trenches backfilled			
	Plumbing trench dug/barricaded			
	SEWER & WATER INSPECTION			
	Plumbing trench backfilled			
	Trenches jetted			
	Electric, phone, cable, gas			
	Plumbing			
	Schedule exterior door delivery			
	Schedule tubs/showers			

Project Log and Checklists (page 4 of 6)

Plan/Elevation _____ Lot # _____

	SCHD Today's Date	SCHD for	Work Complete		SCHD Today's Date	SCH D for	Work Complete
Schedule steel				Framing pick-up			
Framing material drop				Rough plumbing			
Layout/snap lines				Plumbing extras			
Plate				HVAC—gutters/flashing			
Girders/joists installed				Line sets—freon			
Subfloor plumbing				Fireplaces installed			
Subfloor HVAC—ducts				FIREPLACES INSPECTED			
Subfloor electrical				Felt & batt roof			
SUBFLOOR FRAME INSPECTION				Composition/shake roof installed			
Subfloor insulation				Lots scrapped			
SUBFLOOR INSULATION INSPECTION				Tubs/showers covered			
Subfloor decking				Rough HVAC—ducts			
Schedule window installation				Masonry—veneers			
Schedule fireplace installation				Insulate tubs/shear/soffits			
Schedule fireplace chase pans				Flashing for lathers			
Exterior walls framed/stood				Lathers			
Interior walls framed/stood				Hot mop			
Tubs/showers set				Stock sheetrock			
Plumb & line				Stock roof tile			
Electric meters set				Rough electric			
2nd story floor joists				Electrical extras			
Scaffold ordered 2nd story				Frame sweep			
2nd story exterior walls stood				Rough alarm wire			
2nd story interior walls stood				Rough vacuum plumbing			
Tubs/showers set				FRAME INSPECTION			
Plumb & line				VA FRAME INSPECTION			
Trusses delivered				Measure for cabinets			
Trusses installed				Drain/waste/overflow drained			
Order HVAC ducts				Re-cover tubs/showers			
Rafters installed				Wall insulation			
Roof sheathing				INSULATION INSPECTION			
Phone interface/cable box				Order interior doors			
Notify plumbers—start				Furnaces ordered			
Shear installed				Temporary heat for drywall			
ROOF/SHEAR NAIL INSPECTION				Schedule garage doors			
Scaffolding single story				Studs straightened			
Windows installed				Drywall hung			
Siding installed				DRYWALL NAIL INSPECTION			

Project Log and Checklists (page 5 of 6)

Plan/Elevation _____   Lot # _____

	SCHD Today's Date	SCHD for	Work Complete		SCHD Today's Date	SCH D for	Work Complete
GAS LINE PRESSURE INSPECTION				Schedule leaded/etched glass			
Gas meter installed				Pick & rake—graders			
Sheetrock textured				Finish grading			
Walk-through notification—sales				Fencing			
Pipe/sleeves—flatwork				Wrought iron			
Sewer boxes—driveways				Landscaping			
Fireplace faces				Heat for vinyl			
Plastering				Lino scrape			
Downspouts installed				Particle board installed			
STUCCO INSPECTION				Vinyl installed			
Exterior paint				Hardwood floors installed			
Scaffolds down				Base over vinyl/second trim			
Pick & rake flat concrete				Finish hardware			
Flat concrete poured				Bar stools installed			
Order condensing units				Closet shelves installed			
Cabinets delivered				Cabinets adjusted			
Order 1x4/plywood cabinet decking				Plumbing trim			
Kitchen sinks ordered				Appliances installed			
Interior trim				Carpet sweep			
Handrails installed				Carpet installation			
Interior paint				Window coverings installed			
Hardware delivered				Detail house			
Lights delivered				Screens installed			
Order appliances				Fireplace doors installed			
Roofers—lay tile				Gas fireplaces started up			
Cabinets installed				Sidewalks repaired			
Measure for countertops				HVAC start-up/clean furnace filter			
Tile/marble installed				HOUSE FINAL			
Extra tile				VA HOUSE FINAL			
Vanity tops				Paint touch-up			
Shower enclosures/mirrors				Final clean			
HVAC trim				Tub repair			
Formica installed				Silicon showers/tubs			
Electric trim				Garages cleaned			
Finish trim				Finish vacuum			
Windows/tubs cleaned				Garage cabinets installed			
Paint fireplaces/bumper pipe/CAR				Pressure wash concrete			
Schedule screens/fireplace doors				Walk-through			

General Notes (page 6 of 6)

Project Log and Checklists (page 1 of 6)

Parcel # _____ Address _____ Lot # _____

Project # _____ Unit # _____ Phase # _____

Plan # _____ Elevation _____ Permit # _____

When a house is released to build:
order, check, schedule

____ Portable latrines _____

____ Permit #s vs. lot #s vs. address #s _____

____ Plot maps _____

____ Are there storm drains in driveways? _____

____ Sequence sheets _____

____ Locate & mark property pins _____

____ Locate & mark utilities _____

____ Order bumper pipe for garage slabs _____

____ Order mudsill (sleepers) for foundations _____

____ Temporary power pole _____

____ Wash out area for concrete trucks _____

____ Retaining walls _____

____ Steel beams _____

____ Roof materials _____

____ Steel columns _____

____ Trusses _____

____ Exterior doors & pocket door frames _____

____ Windows _____

____ Attic & gable vents _____

____ Termite flashing _____

____ Interior & exterior lights _____

____ Exterior hardware _____

____ Insulation for framers, plumbers, and lathers _____

____ Drywall for framers _____

____ Trash bins set up _____

____ Location from Post Office where mailbox units go ____

____ A.D.A. requirements _____

Daily/Weekly Reminders

____ Call-in time _____

____ Safety meetings _____

____ Progress reports _____

____ SWPPP reports _____

____ Walk models _____

____ Change model flags _____

____ Clean dirt & mud from gutters and storm drains ____

____ Mark electrical panels _____

____ Mark windows _____

____ Order fireplace chase pans _____

____ Order tubs/showers for framers _____

____ Temporary guard/handrails _____

____ Order windows _____

____ Order exterior doors & pocket door frames _____

____ Cover thresholds _____

____ Line sets (freon) _____

____ Cover tubs and showers _____

____ Garage door keys/temporary locks _____

____ Order appliances _____

____ Heat for vinyl/drywall _____

____ Pipe/sleeves for flatwork _____

____ Sewer cleanout boxes _____

____ Retaining walls _____

____ Mailbox pads _____

____ Notify Post Office to set mailbox units _____

____ Lights delivered _____

____ Hardware delivered _____

____ Wrought iron _____

____ Handrails _____

____ Leaded/etched glass _____

____ Condensing units _____

____ Hackouts/broken windows replaced _____

____ Paint fireplaces/bumper pipes/cold air returns _____

____ Floor squeaks fixed before carpet _____

____ Concrete patched before carpet _____

____ Roof gutters cleaned _____

____ Utility companies—final trim _____

____ Sidewalks repaired _____

____ HVAC start-ups _____

____ Return portable latrines _____

Project Log and Checklists (page 2 of 6)

Lot # _____   Address _____   Plan/Elevation _____

Options	Yes	No	Subs Notified	Extras	Yes	No	Subs Notified
Change orders received				Change orders received			
Bedroom/den/retreat				Concrete			
Fireplaces				Backyard landscaping			
2-car garage				Vacuum			
3-car garage				Plumbing			
Sewing room/shop				Electrical			
Ceiling fans				HVAC			
Bedroom lights				Alarm			
Kitchen tile				Garage door opener			
Entry tile				Window coverings			
Opaque glass				R.V. gate (extra wide)			
Microwave oven				Speaker wire			
Finish garage				Interior wall insulation			
Hardwood floors				Wallpaper			
Skylights				Gas log lighter			
Decks				Drywall bullnose corners			
Other:				Other:			

Project Log and Checklists (page 3 of 6)

Plan/Elevation _____ Lot # _____

From Homeowners, Sales Representatives, Office:		SCHD Today's Date	SCHD for	Work Complete
Siding type	Layout/chalk			
Brick type	Trench/excavate			
Stone type	FOOTING INSPECTION			
Stucco type	Forms set			
Garage door style	Sleeves/conduit			
Fireplace model #	Electrical panels			
Roof type /number	Footings poured			
Cabinet colors	STEM WALL INSPECTION			
Paint colors (interior)	Stem walls poured			
	Ground plumbing			
	Plumbing extras			
	GROUND PLUMBING/SETBACK INSPECTION			
Paint colors (exterior)	Termite spray			
	Mechanical extras			
	FOUNDATION INSPECTION			
	VA FOUNDATION INSPECTION			
	Slump/cylinder/saturation tests			
	Slab poured			
Formica selections	GARAGE SLAB INSPECTION			
Tile selections	Bumper pipes installed			
Vinyl selections	Garage slump/cylinder tests			
Carpet selections	Garage slab poured			
Pad size	Foundation waterproofed			
Appliance type	Window wells installed			
Appliance color	Foundation backfilled			
Gutter type	"As Builts" foundation			
Fence type	"As Builts" plumbing			
	TEMPORARY POWER INSPECTION			
	Utility trenches dug/barricaded			
	Trenches backfilled			
	Plumbing trench dug/barricaded			
	SEWER & WATER INSPECTION			
	Plumbing trench backfilled			
	Trenches jetted			
	Electric, phone, cable, gas			
	Plumbing			
	Schedule exterior door delivery			
	Schedule tubs/showers			

Project Log and Checklists (page 4 of 6)

Plan/Elevation _____   Lot # _____

	SCHD Today's Date	SCHD for	Work Complete		SCHD Today's Date	SCHD for	Work Complete
Schedule steel				Framing pick-up			
Framing material drop				Rough plumbing			
Layout/snap lines				Plumbing extras			
Plate				HVAC—gutters/flashing			
Girders/joists installed				Line sets—freon			
Subfloor plumbing				Fireplaces installed			
Subfloor HVAC—ducts				FIREPLACES INSPECTED			
Subfloor electrical				Felt & batt roof			
SUBFLOOR FRAME INSPECTION				Composition/shake roof installed			
Subfloor insulation				Lots scrapped			
SUBFLOOR INSULATION INSPECTION				Tubs/showers covered			
Subfloor decking				Rough HVAC—ducts			
Schedule window installation				Masonry—veneers			
Schedule fireplace installation				Insulate tubs/shear/soffits			
Schedule fireplace chase pans				Flashing for lathers			
Exterior walls framed/stood				Lathers			
Interior walls framed/stood				Hot mop			
Tubs/showers set				Stock sheetrock			
Plumb & line				Stock roof tile			
Electric meters set				Rough electric			
2nd story floor joists				Electrical extras			
Scaffold ordered 2nd story				Frame sweep			
2nd story exterior walls stood				Rough alarm wire			
2nd story interior walls stood				Rough vacuum plumbing			
Tubs/showers set				FRAME INSPECTION			
Plumb & line				VA FRAME INSPECTION			
Trusses delivered				Measure for cabinets			
Trusses installed				Drain/waste/overflow drained			
Order HVAC ducts				Re-cover tubs/showers			
Rafters installed				Wall insulation			
Roof sheathing				INSULATION INSPECTION			
Phone interface/cable box				Order interior doors			
Notify plumbers—start				Furnaces ordered			
Shear installed				Temporary heat for drywall			
ROOF/SHEAR NAIL INSPECTION				Schedule garage doors			
Scaffolding single story				Studs straightened			
Windows installed				Drywall hung			
Siding installed				DRYWALL NAIL INSPECTION			

Project Log and Checklists (page 5 of 6)

Plan/Elevation _____ Lot # _____

	SCHD Today's Date	SCHD for	Work Complete		SCHD Today's Date	SCH D for	Work Complete
GAS LINE PRESSURE INSPECTION				Schedule leaded/etched glass			
Gas meter installed				Pick & rake—graders			
Sheetrock textured				Finish grading			
Walk-through notification—sales				Fencing			
Pipe/sleeves—flatwork				Wrought iron			
Sewer boxes—driveways				Landscaping			
Fireplace faces				Heat for vinyl			
Plastering				Lino scrape			
Downspouts installed				Particle board installed			
STUCCO INSPECTION				Vinyl installed			
Exterior paint				Hardwood floors installed			
Scaffolds down				Base over vinyl/second trim			
Pick & rake flat concrete				Finish hardware			
Flat concrete poured				Bar stools installed			
Order condensing units				Closet shelves installed			
Cabinets delivered				Cabinets adjusted			
Order 1x4/plywood cabinet decking				Plumbing trim			
Kitchen sinks ordered				Appliances installed			
Interior trim				Carpet sweep			
Handrails installed				Carpet installation			
Interior paint				Window coverings installed			
Hardware delivered				Detail house			
Lights delivered				Screens installed			
Order appliances				Fireplace doors installed			
Roofers—lay tile				Gas fireplaces started up			
Cabinets installed				Sidewalks repaired			
Measure for countertops				HVAC start-up/clean furnace filter			
Tile/marble installed				HOUSE FINAL			
Extra tile				VA HOUSE FINAL			
Vanity tops				Paint touch-up			
Shower enclosures/mirrors				Final clean			
HVAC trim				Tub repair			
Formica installed				Silicon showers/tubs			
Electric trim				Garages cleaned			
Finish trim				Finish vacuum			
Windows/tubs cleaned				Garage cabinets installed			
Paint fireplaces/bumper pipe/CAR				Pressure wash concrete			
Schedule screens/fireplace doors				Walk-through			

General Notes (page 6 of 6)

Project Log and Checklists (page 1 of 6)

Parcel # _____   Address _____   Lot # _____
Project # _____   Unit # _____   Phase # _____
Plan # _____   Elevation _____   Permit # _____

When a house is released to build:
order, check, schedule

____ Portable latrines _____
____ Permit #s vs. lot #s vs. address #s _____
____ Plot maps _____
____ Are there storm drains in driveways? _____
____ Sequence sheets _____
____ Locate & mark property pins _____
____ Locate & mark utilities _____
____ Order bumper pipe for garage slabs _____
____ Order mudsill (sleepers) for foundations _____
____ Temporary power pole _____
____ Wash out area for concrete trucks _____
____ Retaining walls _____
____ Steel beams _____
____ Roof materials _____
____ Steel columns _____
____ Trusses _____
____ Exterior doors & pocket door frames _____
____ Windows _____
____ Attic & gable vents _____
____ Termite flashing _____
____ Interior & exterior lights _____
____ Exterior hardware _____
____ Insulation for framers, plumbers, and lathers ____
____ Drywall for framers _____
____ Trash bins set up _____
____ Location from Post Office where mailbox units go ____
____ A.D.A. requirements _____

Daily/Weekly Reminders

____ Call-in time _____
____ Safety meetings _____
____ Progress reports _____
____ SWPPP reports _____
____ Walk models _____
____ Change model flags _____
____ Clean dirt & mud from gutters and storm drains ____
____ Mark electrical panels _____
____ Mark windows _____
____ Order fireplace chase pans _____
____ Order tubs/showers for framers _____
____ Temporary guard/handrails _____
____ Order windows _____
____ Order exterior doors & pocket door frames ____
____ Cover thresholds _____
____ Line sets (freon) _____
____ Cover tubs and showers _____
____ Garage door keys/temporary locks _____
____ Order appliances _____
____ Heat for vinyl/drywall _____
____ Pipe/sleeves for flatwork _____
____ Sewer cleanout boxes _____
____ Retaining walls _____
____ Mailbox pads _____
____ Notify Post Office to set mailbox units _____
____ Lights delivered _____
____ Hardware delivered _____
____ Wrought iron _____
____ Handrails _____
____ Leaded/etched glass _____
____ Condensing units _____
____ Hackouts/broken windows replaced _____
____ Paint fireplaces/bumper pipes/cold air returns ____
____ Floor squeaks fixed before carpet _____
____ Concrete patched before carpet _____
____ Roof gutters cleaned _____
____ Utility companies—final trim _____
____ Sidewalks repaired _____
____ HVAC start-ups _____
____ Return portable latrines _____

Project Log and Checklists (page 2 of 6)

Lot # _____ **Address** _____ **Plan/Elevation** _____

Options	Yes	No	Subs Notified	Extras	Yes	No	Subs Notified
Change orders received				Change orders received			
Bedroom/den/retreat				Concrete			
Fireplaces				Backyard landscaping			
2-car garage				Vacuum			
3-car garage				Plumbing			
Sewing room/shop				Electrical			
Ceiling fans				HVAC			
Bedroom lights				Alarm			
Kitchen tile				Garage door opener			
Entry tile				Window coverings			
Opaque glass				R.V. gate (extra wide)			
Microwave oven				Speaker wire			
Finish garage				Interior wall insulation			
Hardwood floors				Wallpaper			
Skylights				Gas log lighter			
Decks				Drywall bullnose corners			
Other:				Other:			

Project Log and Checklists (page 3 of 6)

Plan/Elevation _____   Lot # _____

From Homeowners, Sales Representatives, Office:		SCHD Today's Date	SCHD for	Work Complete
Siding type	Layout/chalk			
Brick type	Trench/excavate			
Stone type	FOOTING INSPECTION			
Stucco type	Forms set			
Garage door style	Sleeves/conduit			
Fireplace model #	Electrical panels			
Roof type /number	Footings poured			
Cabinet colors	STEM WALL INSPECTION			
Paint colors (interior)	Stem walls poured			
	Ground plumbing			
	Plumbing extras			
	GROUND PLUMBING/SETBACK INSPECTION			
Paint colors (exterior)	Termite spray			
	Mechanical extras			
	FOUNDATION INSPECTION			
	VA FOUNDATION INSPECTION			
	Slump/cylinder/saturation tests			
	Slab poured			
Formica selections	GARAGE SLAB INSPECTION			
Tile selections	Bumper pipes installed			
Vinyl selections	Garage slump/cylinder tests			
Carpet selections	Garage slab poured			
Pad size	Foundation waterproofed			
Appliance type	Window wells installed			
Appliance color	Foundation backfilled			
Gutter type	"As Builts" foundation			
Fence type	"As Builts" plumbing			
	TEMPORARY POWER INSPECTION			
	Utility trenches dug/barricaded			
	Trenches backfilled			
	Plumbing trench dug/barricaded			
	SEWER & WATER INSPECTION			
	Plumbing trench backfilled			
	Trenches jetted			
	Electric, phone, cable, gas			
	Plumbing			
	Schedule exterior door delivery			
	Schedule tubs/showers			

Project Log and Checklists (page 4 of 6)

Plan/Elevation _____ Lot # _____

	SCHD Today's Date	SCHD for	Work Complete		SCHD Today's Date	SCHD for	Work Complete
Schedule steel				Framing pick-up			
Framing material drop				Rough plumbing			
Layout/snap lines				Plumbing extras			
Plate				HVAC—gutters/flashing			
Girders/joists installed				Line sets—freon			
Subfloor plumbing				Fireplaces installed			
Subfloor HVAC—ducts				FIREPLACES INSPECTED			
Subfloor electrical				Felt & batt roof			
SUBFLOOR FRAME INSPECTION				Composition/shake roof installed			
Subfloor insulation				Lots scrapped			
SUBFLOOR INSULATION INSPECTION				Tubs/showers covered			
Subfloor decking				Rough HVAC—ducts			
Schedule window installation				Masonry—veneers			
Schedule fireplace installation				Insulate tubs/shear/soffits			
Schedule fireplace chase pans				Flashing for lathers			
Exterior walls framed/stood				Lathers			
Interior walls framed/stood				Hot mop			
Tubs/showers set				Stock sheetrock			
Plumb & line				Stock roof tile			
Electric meters set				Rough electric			
2nd story floor joists				Electrical extras			
Scaffold ordered 2nd story				Frame sweep			
2nd story exterior walls stood				Rough alarm wire			
2nd story interior walls stood				Rough vacuum plumbing			
Tubs/showers set				FRAME INSPECTION			
Plumb & line				VA FRAME INSPECTION			
Trusses delivered				Measure for cabinets			
Trusses installed				Drain/waste/overflow drained			
Order HVAC ducts				Re-cover tubs/showers			
Rafters installed				Wall insulation			
Roof sheathing				INSULATION INSPECTION			
Phone interface/cable box				Order interior doors			
Notify plumbers—start				Furnaces ordered			
Shear installed				Temporary heat for drywall			
ROOF/SHEAR NAIL INSPECTION				Schedule garage doors			
Scaffolding single story				Studs straightened			
Windows installed				Drywall hung			
Siding installed				DRYWALL NAIL INSPECTION			

Project Log and Checklists (page 5 of 6)

Plan/Elevation _____ Lot # _____

	SCHD Today's Date	SCHD for	Work Complete		SCHD Today's Date	SCH D for	Work Complete
GAS LINE PRESSURE INSPECTION				Schedule leaded/etched glass			
Gas meter installed				Pick & rake—graders			
Sheetrock textured				Finish grading			
Walk-through notification—sales				Fencing			
Pipe/sleeves—flatwork				Wrought iron			
Sewer boxes—driveways				Landscaping			
Fireplace faces				Heat for vinyl			
Plastering				Lino scrape			
Downspouts installed				Particle board installed			
STUCCO INSPECTION				Vinyl installed			
Exterior paint				Hardwood floors installed			
Scaffolds down				Base over vinyl/second trim			
Pick & rake flat concrete				Finish hardware			
Flat concrete poured				Bar stools installed			
Order condensing units				Closet shelves installed			
Cabinets delivered				Cabinets adjusted			
Order 1x4/plywood cabinet decking				Plumbing trim			
Kitchen sinks ordered				Appliances installed			
Interior trim				Carpet sweep			
Handrails installed				Carpet installation			
Interior paint				Window coverings installed			
Hardware delivered				Detail house			
Lights delivered				Screens installed			
Order appliances				Fireplace doors installed			
Roofers—lay tile				Gas fireplaces started up			
Cabinets installed				Sidewalks repaired			
Measure for countertops				HVAC start-up/clean furnace filter			
Tile/marble installed				HOUSE FINAL			
Extra tile				VA HOUSE FINAL			
Vanity tops				Paint touch-up			
Shower enclosures/mirrors				Final clean			
HVAC trim				Tub repair			
Formica installed				Silicon showers/tubs			
Electric trim				Garages cleaned			
Finish trim				Finish vacuum			
Windows/tubs cleaned				Garage cabinets installed			
Paint fireplaces/bumper pipe/CAR				Pressure wash concrete			
Schedule screens/fireplace doors				Walk-through			

General Notes (page 6 of 6)

Project Log and Checklists (page 1 of 6)

Parcel # _____   Address _____   Lot # _____
Project # _____   Unit # _____   Phase # _____
Plan # _____   Elevation _____   Permit # _____

When a house is released to build: order, check, schedule

____ Portable latrines _____
____ Permit #s vs. lot #s vs. address #s _____
____ Plot maps _____
____ Are there storm drains in driveways? _____
____ Sequence sheets _____
____ Locate & mark property pins _____
____ Locate & mark utilities _____
____ Order bumper pipe for garage slabs _____
____ Order mudsill (sleepers) for foundations _____
____ Temporary power pole _____
____ Wash out area for concrete trucks _____
____ Retaining walls _____
____ Steel beams _____
____ Roof materials _____
____ Steel columns _____
____ Trusses _____
____ Exterior doors & pocket door frames _____
____ Windows _____
____ Attic & gable vents _____
____ Termite flashing _____
____ Interior & exterior lights _____
____ Exterior hardware _____
____ Insulation for framers, plumbers, and lathers _____
____ Drywall for framers _____
____ Trash bins set up _____
____ Location from Post Office where mailbox units go ____
____ A.D.A. requirements _____

Daily/Weekly Reminders

____ Call-in time _____
____ Safety meetings _____
____ Progress reports _____
____ SWPPP reports _____
____ Walk models _____
____ Change model flags _____
____ Clean dirt & mud from gutters and storm drains ____
____ Mark electrical panels _____
____ Mark windows _____
____ Order fireplace chase pans _____
____ Order tubs/showers for framers _____
____ Temporary guard/handrails _____
____ Order windows _____
____ Order exterior doors & pocket door frames ____
____ Cover thresholds _____
____ Line sets (freon) _____
____ Cover tubs and showers _____
____ Garage door keys/temporary locks _____
____ Order appliances _____
____ Heat for vinyl/drywall _____
____ Pipe/sleeves for flatwork _____
____ Sewer cleanout boxes _____
____ Retaining walls _____
____ Mailbox pads _____
____ Notify Post Office to set mailbox units _____
____ Lights delivered _____
____ Hardware delivered _____
____ Wrought iron _____
____ Handrails _____
____ Leaded/etched glass _____
____ Condensing units _____
____ Hackouts/broken windows replaced _____
____ Paint fireplaces/bumper pipes/cold air returns ____
____ Floor squeaks fixed before carpet _____
____ Concrete patched before carpet _____
____ Roof gutters cleaned _____
____ Utility companies—final trim _____
____ Sidewalks repaired _____
____ HVAC start-ups _____
____ Return portable latrines _____

Project Log and Checklists (page 2 of 6)

Lot # _____   Address _____   Plan/Elevation _____

Options	Yes	No	Subs Notified	Extras	Yes	No	Subs Notified
Change orders received				Change orders received			
Bedroom/den/retreat				Concrete			
Fireplaces				Backyard landscaping			
2-car garage				Vacuum			
3-car garage				Plumbing			
Sewing room/shop				Electrical			
Ceiling fans				HVAC			
Bedroom lights				Alarm			
Kitchen tile				Garage door opener			
Entry tile				Window coverings			
Opaque glass				R.V. gate (extra wide)			
Microwave oven				Speaker wire			
Finish garage				Interior wall insulation			
Hardwood floors				Wallpaper			
Skylights				Gas log lighter			
Decks				Drywall bullnose corners			
Other:				Other:			

Project Log and Checklists (page 3 of 6)

Plan/Elevation _____   Lot # _____

From Homeowners, Sales Representatives, Office:		SCHD Today's Date	SCHD for	Work Complete
Siding type	Layout/chalk			
Brick type	Trench/excavate			
Stone type	FOOTING INSPECTION			
Stucco type	Forms set			
Garage door style	Sleeves/conduit			
Fireplace model #	Electrical panels			
Roof type /number	Footings poured			
Cabinet colors	STEM WALL INSPECTION			
Paint colors (interior)	Stem walls poured			
	Ground plumbing			
	Plumbing extras			
	GROUND PLUMBING/SETBACK INSPECTION			
Paint colors (exterior)	Termite spray			
	Mechanical extras			
	FOUNDATION INSPECTION			
	VA FOUNDATION INSPECTION			
	Slump/cylinder/saturation tests			
	Slab poured			
Formica selections	GARAGE SLAB INSPECTION			
Tile selections	Bumper pipes installed			
Vinyl selections	Garage slump/cylinder tests			
Carpet selections	Garage slab poured			
Pad size	Foundation waterproofed			
Appliance type	Window wells installed			
Appliance color	Foundation backfilled			
Gutter type	"As Builts" foundation			
Fence type	"As Builts" plumbing			
	TEMPORARY POWER INSPECTION			
	Utility trenches dug/barricaded			
	Trenches backfilled			
	Plumbing trench dug/barricaded			
	SEWER & WATER INSPECTION			
	Plumbing trench backfilled			
	Trenches jetted			
	Electric, phone, cable, gas			
	Plumbing			
	Schedule exterior door delivery			
	Schedule tubs/showers			

Project Log and Checklists (page 4 of 6)

Plan/Elevation _____ Lot # _____

	SCHD Today's Date	SCHD for	Work Complete		SCHD Today's Date	SCH D for	Work Complete
Schedule steel				Framing pick-up			
Framing material drop				Rough plumbing			
Layout/snap lines				Plumbing extras			
Plate				HVAC—gutters/flashing			
Girders/joists installed				Line sets—freon			
Subfloor plumbing				Fireplaces installed			
Subfloor HVAC—ducts				FIREPLACES INSPECTED			
Subfloor electrical				Felt & batt roof			
SUBFLOOR FRAME INSPECTION				Composition/shake roof installed			
Subfloor insulation				Lots scrapped			
SUBFLOOR INSULATION INSPECTION				Tubs/showers covered			
Subfloor decking				Rough HVAC—ducts			
Schedule window installation				Masonry—veneers			
Schedule fireplace installation				Insulate tubs/shear/soffits			
Schedule fireplace chase pans				Flashing for lathers			
Exterior walls framed/stood				Lathers			
Interior walls framed/stood				Hot mop			
Tubs/showers set				Stock sheetrock			
Plumb & line				Stock roof tile			
Electric meters set				Rough electric			
2nd story floor joists				Electrical extras			
Scaffold ordered 2nd story				Frame sweep			
2nd story exterior walls stood				Rough alarm wire			
2nd story interior walls stood				Rough vacuum plumbing			
Tubs/showers set				FRAME INSPECTION			
Plumb & line				VA FRAME INSPECTION			
Trusses delivered				Measure for cabinets			
Trusses installed				Drain/waste/overflow drained			
Order HVAC ducts				Re-cover tubs/showers			
Rafters installed				Wall insulation			
Roof sheathing				INSULATION INSPECTION			
Phone interface/cable box				Order interior doors			
Notify plumbers—start				Furnaces ordered			
Shear installed				Temporary heat for drywall			
ROOF/SHEAR NAIL INSPECTION				Schedule garage doors			
Scaffolding single story				Studs straightened			
Windows installed				Drywall hung			
Siding installed				DRYWALL NAIL INSPECTION			

Project Log and Checklists (page 5 of 6)

Plan/Elevation _____ Lot # _____

	SCHD Today's Date	SCHD for	Work Complete		SCHD Today's Date	SCHD for	Work Complete
GAS LINE PRESSURE INSPECTION				Schedule leaded/etched glass			
Gas meter installed				Pick & rake—graders			
Sheetrock textured				Finish grading			
Walk-through notification—sales				Fencing			
Pipe/sleeves—flatwork				Wrought iron			
Sewer boxes—driveways				Landscaping			
Fireplace faces				Heat for vinyl			
Plastering				Lino scrape			
Downspouts installed				Particle board installed			
STUCCO INSPECTION				Vinyl installed			
Exterior paint				Hardwood floors installed			
Scaffolds down				Base over vinyl/second trim			
Pick & rake flat concrete				Finish hardware			
Flat concrete poured				Bar stools installed			
Order condensing units				Closet shelves installed			
Cabinets delivered				Cabinets adjusted			
Order 1x4/plywood cabinet decking				Plumbing trim			
Kitchen sinks ordered				Appliances installed			
Interior trim				Carpet sweep			
Handrails installed				Carpet installation			
Interior paint				Window coverings installed			
Hardware delivered				Detail house			
Lights delivered				Screens installed			
Order appliances				Fireplace doors installed			
Roofers—lay tile				Gas fireplaces started up			
Cabinets installed				Sidewalks repaired			
Measure for countertops				HVAC start-up/clean furnace filter			
Tile/marble installed				HOUSE FINAL			
Extra tile				VA HOUSE FINAL			
Vanity tops				Paint touch-up			
Shower enclosures/mirrors				Final clean			
HVAC trim				Tub repair			
Formica installed				Silicon showers/tubs			
Electric trim				Garages cleaned			
Finish trim				Finish vacuum			
Windows/tubs cleaned				Garage cabinets installed			
Paint fireplaces/bumper pipe/CAR				Pressure wash concrete			
Schedule screens/fireplace doors				Walk-through			

General Notes (page 6 of 6)

Project Log and Checklists (page 1 of 6)

Parcel # _____   Address _____   Lot # _____
Project # _____   Unit # _____   Phase # _____
Plan # _____   Elevation _____   Permit # _____

**When a house is released to build:
order, check, schedule**

____ Portable latrines _____
____ Permit #s vs. lot #s vs. address #s _____
____ Plot maps _____
____ Are there storm drains in driveways? _____
____ Sequence sheets _____
____ Locate & mark property pins _____
____ Locate & mark utilities _____
____ Order bumper pipe for garage slabs _____
____ Order mudsill (sleepers) for foundations _____
____ Temporary power pole _____
____ Wash out area for concrete trucks _____
____ Retaining walls _____
____ Steel beams _____
____ Roof materials _____
____ Steel columns _____
____ Trusses _____
____ Exterior doors & pocket door frames _____
____ Windows _____
____ Attic & gable vents _____
____ Termite flashing _____
____ Interior & exterior lights _____
____ Exterior hardware _____
____ Insulation for framers, plumbers, and lathers ____
____ Drywall for framers _____
____ Trash bins set up _____
____ Location from Post Office where mailbox units go __
____ A.D.A. requirements _____

Daily/Weekly Reminders

____ Call-in time _____
____ Safety meetings _____
____ Progress reports _____
____ SWPPP reports _____
____ Walk models _____
____ Change model flags _____
____ Clean dirt & mud from gutters and storm drains ____
____ Mark electrical panels _____
____ Mark windows _____
____ Order fireplace chase pans _____
____ Order tubs/showers for framers _____
____ Temporary guard/handrails _____
____ Order windows _____
____ Order exterior doors & pocket door frames _____
____ Cover thresholds _____
____ Line sets (freon) _____
____ Cover tubs and showers _____
____ Garage door keys/temporary locks _____
____ Order appliances _____
____ Heat for vinyl/drywall _____
____ Pipe/sleeves for flatwork _____
____ Sewer cleanout boxes _____
____ Retaining walls _____
____ Mailbox pads _____
____ Notify Post Office to set mailbox units _____
____ Lights delivered _____
____ Hardware delivered _____
____ Wrought iron _____
____ Handrails _____
____ Leaded/etched glass _____
____ Condensing units _____
____ Hackouts/broken windows replaced _____
____ Paint fireplaces/bumper pipes/cold air returns ____
____ Floor squeaks fixed before carpet _____
____ Concrete patched before carpet _____
____ Roof gutters cleaned _____
____ Utility companies—final trim _____
____ Sidewalks repaired _____
____ HVAC start-ups _____
____ Return portable latrines _____

Project Log and Checklists (page 2 of 6)

Lot # _____   Address _____   Plan/Elevation _____

Options	Yes	No	Subs Notified	Extras	Yes	No	Subs Notified
Change orders received				Change orders received			
Bedroom/den/retreat				Concrete			
Fireplaces				Backyard landscaping			
2-car garage				Vacuum			
3-car garage				Plumbing			
Sewing room/shop				Electrical			
Ceiling fans				HVAC			
Bedroom lights				Alarm			
Kitchen tile				Garage door opener			
Entry tile				Window coverings			
Opaque glass				R.V. gate (extra wide)			
Microwave oven				Speaker wire			
Finish garage				Interior wall insulation			
Hardwood floors				Wallpaper			
Skylights				Gas log lighter			
Decks				Drywall bullnose corners			
Other:				Other:			

Project Log and Checklists (page 3 of 6)

Plan/Elevation _____   Lot # _____

From Homeowners, Sales Representatives, Office:		SCHD Today's Date	SCHD for	Work Complete
Siding type	Layout/chalk			
Brick type	Trench/excavate			
Stone type	FOOTING INSPECTION			
Stucco type	Forms set			
Garage door style	Sleeves/conduit			
Fireplace model #	Electrical panels			
Roof type /number	Footings poured			
Cabinet colors	STEM WALL INSPECTION			
Paint colors (interior)	Stem walls poured			
	Ground plumbing			
	Plumbing extras			
	GROUND PLUMBING/SETBACK INSPECTION			
Paint colors (exterior)	Termite spray			
	Mechanical extras			
	FOUNDATION INSPECTION			
	VA FOUNDATION INSPECTION			
	Slump/cylinder/saturation tests			
	Slab poured			
Formica selections	GARAGE SLAB INSPECTION			
Tile selections	Bumper pipes installed			
Vinyl selections	Garage slump/cylinder tests			
Carpet selections	Garage slab poured			
Pad size	Foundation waterproofed			
Appliance type	Window wells installed			
Appliance color	Foundation backfilled			
Gutter type	"As Builts" foundation			
Fence type	"As Builts" plumbing			
	TEMPORARY POWER INSPECTION			
	Utility trenches dug/barricaded			
	Trenches backfilled			
	Plumbing trench dug/barricaded			
	SEWER & WATER INSPECTION			
	Plumbing trench backfilled			
	Trenches jetted			
	Electric, phone, cable, gas			
	Plumbing			
	Schedule exterior door delivery			
	Schedule tubs/showers			

Project Log and Checklists (page 4 of 6)

Plan/Elevation _____   Lot # _____

	SCHD Today's Date	SCHD for	Work Complete		SCHD Today's Date	SCH D for	Work Complete
Schedule steel				Framing pick-up			
Framing material drop				Rough plumbing			
Layout/snap lines				Plumbing extras			
Plate				HVAC—gutters/flashing			
Girders/joists installed				Line sets—freon			
Subfloor plumbing				Fireplaces installed			
Subfloor HVAC—ducts				FIREPLACES INSPECTED			
Subfloor electrical				Felt & batt roof			
SUBFLOOR FRAME INSPECTION				Composition/shake roof installed			
Subfloor insulation				Lots scrapped			
SUBFLOOR INSULATION INSPECTION				Tubs/showers covered			
Subfloor decking				Rough HVAC—ducts			
Schedule window installation				Masonry—veneers			
Schedule fireplace installation				Insulate tubs/shear/soffits			
Schedule fireplace chase pans				Flashing for lathers			
Exterior walls framed/stood				Lathers			
Interior walls framed/stood				Hot mop			
Tubs/showers set				Stock sheetrock			
Plumb & line				Stock roof tile			
Electric meters set				Rough electric			
2nd story floor joists				Electrical extras			
Scaffold ordered 2nd story				Frame sweep			
2nd story exterior walls stood				Rough alarm wire			
2nd story interior walls stood				Rough vacuum plumbing			
Tubs/showers set				FRAME INSPECTION			
Plumb & line				VA FRAME INSPECTION			
Trusses delivered				Measure for cabinets			
Trusses installed				Drain/waste/overflow drained			
Order HVAC ducts				Re-cover tubs/showers			
Rafters installed				Wall insulation			
Roof sheathing				INSULATION INSPECTION			
Phone interface/cable box				Order interior doors			
Notify plumbers—start				Furnaces ordered			
Shear installed				Temporary heat for drywall			
ROOF/SHEAR NAIL INSPECTION				Schedule garage doors			
Scaffolding single story				Studs straightened			
Windows installed				Drywall hung			
Siding installed				DRYWALL NAIL INSPECTION			

Project Log and Checklists (page 5 of 6)

Plan/Elevation _____ Lot # _____

	SCHD Today's Date	SCHD for	Work Complete		SCHD Today's Date	SCH D for	Work Complete
GAS LINE PRESSURE INSPECTION				Schedule leaded/etched glass			
Gas meter installed				Pick & rake—graders			
Sheetrock textured				Finish grading			
Walk-through notification—sales				Fencing			
Pipe/sleeves—flatwork				Wrought iron			
Sewer boxes—driveways				Landscaping			
Fireplace faces				Heat for vinyl			
Plastering				Lino scrape			
Downspouts installed				Particle board installed			
STUCCO INSPECTION				Vinyl installed			
Exterior paint				Hardwood floors installed			
Scaffolds down				Base over vinyl/second trim			
Pick & rake flat concrete				Finish hardware			
Flat concrete poured				Bar stools installed			
Order condensing units				Closet shelves installed			
Cabinets delivered				Cabinets adjusted			
Order 1x4/plywood cabinet decking				Plumbing trim			
Kitchen sinks ordered				Appliances installed			
Interior trim				Carpet sweep			
Handrails installed				Carpet installation			
Interior paint				Window coverings installed			
Hardware delivered				Detail house			
Lights delivered				Screens installed			
Order appliances				Fireplace doors installed			
Roofers—lay tile				Gas fireplaces started up			
Cabinets installed				Sidewalks repaired			
Measure for countertops				HVAC start-up/clean furnace filter			
Tile/marble installed				HOUSE FINAL			
Extra tile				VA HOUSE FINAL			
Vanity tops				Paint touch-up			
Shower enclosures/mirrors				Final clean			
HVAC trim				Tub repair			
Formica installed				Silicon showers/tubs			
Electric trim				Garages cleaned			
Finish trim				Finish vacuum			
Windows/tubs cleaned				Garage cabinets installed			
Paint fireplaces/bumper pipe/CAR				Pressure wash concrete			
Schedule screens/fireplace doors				Walk-through			

General Notes (page 6 of 6)

Project Log and Checklists (page 1 of 6)

Parcel # _____ Address _____ Lot # _____
Project # _____ Unit # _____ Phase # _____
Plan # _____ Elevation _____ Permit # _____

**When a house is released to build:
order, check, schedule**

- ____ Portable latrines _____
- ____ Permit #s vs. lot #s vs. address #s _____
- ____ Plot maps _____
- ____ Are there storm drains in driveways? _____
- ____ Sequence sheets _____
- ____ Locate & mark property pins _____
- ____ Locate & mark utilities _____
- ____ Order bumper pipe for garage slabs _____
- ____ Order mudsill (sleepers) for foundations _____
- ____ Temporary power pole _____
- ____ Wash out area for concrete trucks _____
- ____ Retaining walls _____
- ____ Steel beams _____
- ____ Roof materials _____
- ____ Steel columns _____
- ____ Trusses _____
- ____ Exterior doors & pocket door frames _____
- ____ Windows _____
- ____ Attic & gable vents _____
- ____ Termite flashing _____
- ____ Interior & exterior lights _____
- ____ Exterior hardware _____
- ____ Insulation for framers, plumbers, and lathers _____
- ____ Drywall for framers _____
- ____ Trash bins set up _____
- ____ Location from Post Office where mailbox units go __
- ____ A.D.A. requirements _____

Daily/Weekly Reminders

- ____ Call-in time _____
- ____ Safety meetings _____
- ____ Progress reports _____
- ____ SWPPP reports _____
- ____ Walk models _____
- ____ Change model flags _____
- ____ Clean dirt & mud from gutters and storm drains ____
- ____ Mark electrical panels _____
- ____ Mark windows _____
- ____ Order fireplace chase pans _____
- ____ Order tubs/showers for framers _____
- ____ Temporary guard/handrails _____
- ____ Order windows _____
- ____ Order exterior doors & pocket door frames _____
- ____ Cover thresholds _____
- ____ Line sets (freon) _____
- ____ Cover tubs and showers _____
- ____ Garage door keys/temporary locks _____
- ____ Order appliances _____
- ____ Heat for vinyl/drywall _____
- ____ Pipe/sleeves for flatwork _____
- ____ Sewer cleanout boxes _____
- ____ Retaining walls _____
- ____ Mailbox pads _____
- ____ Notify Post Office to set mailbox units _____
- ____ Lights delivered _____
- ____ Hardware delivered _____
- ____ Wrought iron _____
- ____ Handrails _____
- ____ Leaded/etched glass _____
- ____ Condensing units _____
- ____ Hackouts/broken windows replaced _____
- ____ Paint fireplaces/bumper pipes/cold air returns ____
- ____ Floor squeaks fixed before carpet _____
- ____ Concrete patched before carpet _____
- ____ Roof gutters cleaned _____
- ____ Utility companies—final trim _____
- ____ Sidewalks repaired _____
- ____ HVAC start-ups _____
- ____ Return portable latrines

Project Log and Checklists (page 2 of 6)

Lot # _____   Address _____   Plan/Elevation _____

Options	Yes	No	Subs Notified	Extras	Yes	No	Subs Notified
Change orders received				Change orders received			
Bedroom/den/retreat				Concrete			
Fireplaces				Backyard landscaping			
2-car garage				Vacuum			
3-car garage				Plumbing			
Sewing room/shop				Electrical			
Ceiling fans				HVAC			
Bedroom lights				Alarm			
Kitchen tile				Garage door opener			
Entry tile				Window coverings			
Opaque glass				R.V. gate (extra wide)			
Microwave oven				Speaker wire			
Finish garage				Interior wall insulation			
Hardwood floors				Wallpaper			
Skylights				Gas log lighter			
Decks				Drywall bullnose corners			
Other:				Other:			

Project Log and Checklists (page 3 of 6)

Plan/Elevation _____ Lot # _____

From Homeowners, Sales Representatives, Office:		SCHD Today's Date	SCHD for	Work Complete
Siding type	Layout/chalk			
Brick type	Trench/excavate			
Stone type	FOOTING INSPECTION			
Stucco type	Forms set			
Garage door style	Sleeves/conduit			
Fireplace model #	Electrical panels			
Roof type /number	Footings poured			
Cabinet colors	STEM WALL INSPECTION			
Paint colors (interior)	Stem walls poured			
	Ground plumbing			
	Plumbing extras			
	GROUND PLUMBING/SETBACK INSPECTION			
Paint colors (exterior)	Termite spray			
	Mechanical extras			
	FOUNDATION INSPECTION			
	VA FOUNDATION INSPECTION			
	Slump/cylinder/saturation tests			
	Slab poured			
Formica selections	GARAGE SLAB INSPECTION			
Tile selections	Bumper pipes installed			
Vinyl selections	Garage slump/cylinder tests			
Carpet selections	Garage slab poured			
Pad size	Foundation waterproofed			
Appliance type	Window wells installed			
Appliance color	Foundation backfilled			
Gutter type	"As Builts" foundation			
Fence type	"As Builts" plumbing			
	TEMPORARY POWER INSPECTION			
	Utility trenches dug/barricaded			
	Trenches backfilled			
	Plumbing trench dug/barricaded			
	SEWER & WATER INSPECTION			
	Plumbing trench backfilled			
	Trenches jetted			
	Electric, phone, cable, gas			
	Plumbing			
	Schedule exterior door delivery			
	Schedule tubs/showers			

Project Log and Checklists (page 4 of 6)

Plan/Elevation _____ Lot # _____

	SCHD Today's Date	SCHD for	Work Complete		SCHD Today's Date	SCH D for	Work Complete
Schedule steel				Framing pick-up			
Framing material drop				Rough plumbing			
Layout/snap lines				Plumbing extras			
Plate				HVAC—gutters/flashing			
Girders/joists installed				Line sets—freon			
Subfloor plumbing				Fireplaces installed			
Subfloor HVAC—ducts				FIREPLACES INSPECTED			
Subfloor electrical				Felt & batt roof			
SUBFLOOR FRAME INSPECTION				Composition/shake roof installed			
Subfloor insulation				Lots scrapped			
SUBFLOOR INSULATION INSPECTION				Tubs/showers covered			
Subfloor decking				Rough HVAC—ducts			
Schedule window installation				Masonry—veneers			
Schedule fireplace installation				Insulate tubs/shear/soffits			
Schedule fireplace chase pans				Flashing for lathers			
Exterior walls framed/stood				Lathers			
Interior walls framed/stood				Hot mop			
Tubs/showers set				Stock sheetrock			
Plumb & line				Stock roof tile			
Electric meters set				Rough electric			
2nd story floor joists				Electrical extras			
Scaffold ordered 2nd story				Frame sweep			
2nd story exterior walls stood				Rough alarm wire			
2nd story interior walls stood				Rough vacuum plumbing			
Tubs/showers set				FRAME INSPECTION			
Plumb & line				VA FRAME INSPECTION			
Trusses delivered				Measure for cabinets			
Trusses installed				Drain/waste/overflow drained			
Order HVAC ducts				Re-cover tubs/showers			
Rafters installed				Wall insulation			
Roof sheathing				INSULATION INSPECTION			
Phone interface/cable box				Order interior doors			
Notify plumbers—start				Furnaces ordered			
Shear installed				Temporary heat for drywall			
ROOF/SHEAR NAIL INSPECTION				Schedule garage doors			
Scaffolding single story				Studs straightened			
Windows installed				Drywall hung			
Siding installed				DRYWALL NAIL INSPECTION			

Project Log and Checklists (page 5 of 6)

Plan/Elevation _____ Lot # _____

	SCHD Today's Date	SCHD for	Work Complete		SCHD Today's Date	SCH D for	Work Complete
GAS LINE PRESSURE INSPECTION				Schedule leaded/etched glass			
Gas meter installed				Pick & rake—graders			
Sheetrock textured				Finish grading			
Walk-through notification—sales				Fencing			
Pipe/sleeves—flatwork				Wrought iron			
Sewer boxes—driveways				Landscaping			
Fireplace faces				Heat for vinyl			
Plastering				Lino scrape			
Downspouts installed				Particle board installed			
STUCCO INSPECTION				Vinyl installed			
Exterior paint				Hardwood floors installed			
Scaffolds down				Base over vinyl/second trim			
Pick & rake flat concrete				Finish hardware			
Flat concrete poured				Bar stools installed			
Order condensing units				Closet shelves installed			
Cabinets delivered				Cabinets adjusted			
Order 1x4/plywood cabinet decking				Plumbing trim			
Kitchen sinks ordered				Appliances installed			
Interior trim				Carpet sweep			
Handrails installed				Carpet installation			
Interior paint				Window coverings installed			
Hardware delivered				Detail house			
Lights delivered				Screens installed			
Order appliances				Fireplace doors installed			
Roofers—lay tile				Gas fireplaces started up			
Cabinets installed				Sidewalks repaired			
Measure for countertops				HVAC start-up/clean furnace filter			
Tile/marble installed				HOUSE FINAL			
Extra tile				VA HOUSE FINAL			
Vanity tops				Paint touch-up			
Shower enclosures/mirrors				Final clean			
HVAC trim				Tub repair			
Formica installed				Silicon showers/tubs			
Electric trim				Garages cleaned			
Finish trim				Finish vacuum			
Windows/tubs cleaned				Garage cabinets installed			
Paint fireplaces/bumper pipe/CAR				Pressure wash concrete			
Schedule screens/fireplace doors				Walk-through			

General Notes (page 6 of 6)

Project Log and Checklists (page 1 of 6)

Parcel # _____ Address _____ Lot # _____

Project #_____ Unit # _____ Phase # _____

Plan # _____ Elevation _____ Permit # _____

**When a house is released to build:
order, check, schedule**

- ____ Portable latrines _____
- ____ Permit #s vs. lot #s vs. address #s _____
- ____ Plot maps _____
- ____ Are there storm drains in driveways? _____
- ____ Sequence sheets _____
- ____ Locate & mark property pins _____
- ____ Locate & mark utilities _____
- ____ Order bumper pipe for garage slabs _____
- ____ Order mudsill (sleepers) for foundations _____
- ____ Temporary power pole _____
- ____ Wash out area for concrete trucks _____
- ____ Retaining walls _____
- ____ Steel beams _____
- ____ Roof materials _____
- ____ Steel columns _____
- ____ Trusses _____
- ____ Exterior doors & pocket door frames _____
- ____ Windows _____
- ____ Attic & gable vents _____
- ____ Termite flashing _____
- ____ Interior & exterior lights _____
- ____ Exterior hardware _____
- ____ Insulation for framers, plumbers, and lathers ____
- ____ Drywall for framers _____
- ____ Trash bins set up _____
- ____ Location from Post Office where mailbox units go __
- ____ A.D.A. requirements _____

Daily/Weekly Reminders

- ____ Call-in time _____
- ____ Safety meetings _____
- ____ Progress reports _____
- ____ SWPPP reports _____
- ____ Walk models _____
- ____ Change model flags _____
- ____ Clean dirt & mud from gutters and storm drains ____
- ____ Mark electrical panels _____
- ____ Mark windows _____
- ____ Order fireplace chase pans _____
- ____ Order tubs/showers for framers _____
- ____ Temporary guard/handrails _____
- ____ Order windows _____
- ____ Order exterior doors & pocket door frames _____
- ____ Cover thresholds _____
- ____ Line sets (freon) _____
- ____ Cover tubs and showers _____
- ____ Garage door keys/temporary locks _____
- ____ Order appliances _____
- ____ Heat for vinyl/drywall _____
- ____ Pipe/sleeves for flatwork _____
- ____ Sewer cleanout boxes _____
- ____ Retaining walls _____
- ____ Mailbox pads _____
- ____ Notify Post Office to set mailbox units _____
- ____ Lights delivered _____
- ____ Hardware delivered _____
- ____ Wrought iron _____
- ____ Handrails _____
- ____ Leaded/etched glass _____
- ____ Condensing units _____
- ____ Hackouts/broken windows replaced _____
- ____ Paint fireplaces/bumper pipes/cold air returns ____
- ____ Floor squeaks fixed before carpet _____
- ____ Concrete patched before carpet _____
- ____ Roof gutters cleaned _____
- ____ Utility companies—final trim _____
- ____ Sidewalks repaired _____
- ____ HVAC start-ups _____
- ____ Return portable latrines _____

Project Log and Checklists (page 2 of 6)

Lot # _____   Address _____   Plan/Elevation _____

Options	Yes	No	Subs Notified	Extras	Yes	No	Subs Notified
Change orders received				Change orders received			
Bedroom/den/retreat				Concrete			
Fireplaces				Backyard landscaping			
2-car garage				Vacuum			
3-car garage				Plumbing			
Sewing room/shop				Electrical			
Ceiling fans				HVAC			
Bedroom lights				Alarm			
Kitchen tile				Garage door opener			
Entry tile				Window coverings			
Opaque glass				R.V. gate (extra wide)			
Microwave oven				Speaker wire			
Finish garage				Interior wall insulation			
Hardwood floors				Wallpaper			
Skylights				Gas log lighter			
Decks				Drywall bullnose corners			
Other:				Other:			

Project Log and Checklists (page 3 of 6)

Plan/Elevation _____   Lot # _____

From Homeowners, Sales Representatives, Office:		SCHD Today's Date	SCHD for	Work Complete
Siding type	Layout/chalk			
Brick type	Trench/excavate			
Stone type	FOOTING INSPECTION			
Stucco type	Forms set			
Garage door style	Sleeves/conduit			
Fireplace model #	Electrical panels			
Roof type /number	Footings poured			
Cabinet colors	STEM WALL INSPECTION			
Paint colors (interior)	Stem walls poured			
	Ground plumbing			
	Plumbing extras			
	GROUND PLUMBING/SETBACK INSPECTION			
Paint colors (exterior)	Termite spray			
	Mechanical extras			
	FOUNDATION INSPECTION			
	VA FOUNDATION INSPECTION			
	Slump/cylinder/saturation tests			
	Slab poured			
Formica selections	GARAGE SLAB INSPECTION			
Tile selections	Bumper pipes installed			
Vinyl selections	Garage slump/cylinder tests			
Carpet selections	Garage slab poured			
Pad size	Foundation waterproofed			
Appliance type	Window wells installed			
Appliance color	Foundation backfilled			
Gutter type	"As Builts" foundation			
Fence type	"As Builts" plumbing			
	TEMPORARY POWER INSPECTION			
	Utility trenches dug/barricaded			
	Trenches backfilled			
	Plumbing trench dug/barricaded			
	SEWER & WATER INSPECTION			
	Plumbing trench backfilled			
	Trenches jetted			
	Electric, phone, cable, gas			
	Plumbing			
	Schedule exterior door delivery			
	Schedule tubs/showers			

Project Log and Checklists (page 4 of 6)

Plan/Elevation _____ Lot # _____

	SCHD Today's Date	SCHD for	Work Complete		SCHD Today's Date	SCH D for	Work Complete
Schedule steel				Framing pick-up			
Framing material drop				Rough plumbing			
Layout/snap lines				Plumbing extras			
Plate				HVAC—gutters/flashing			
Girders/joists installed				Line sets—freon			
Subfloor plumbing				Fireplaces installed			
Subfloor HVAC—ducts				FIREPLACES INSPECTED			
Subfloor electrical				Felt & batt roof			
SUBFLOOR FRAME INSPECTION				Composition/shake roof installed			
Subfloor insulation				Lots scrapped			
SUBFLOOR INSULATION INSPECTION				Tubs/showers covered			
Subfloor decking				Rough HVAC—ducts			
Schedule window installation				Masonry—veneers			
Schedule fireplace installation				Insulate tubs/shear/soffits			
Schedule fireplace chase pans				Flashing for lathers			
Exterior walls framed/stood				Lathers			
Interior walls framed/stood				Hot mop			
Tubs/showers set				Stock sheetrock			
Plumb & line				Stock roof tile			
Electric meters set				Rough electric			
2nd story floor joists				Electrical extras			
Scaffold ordered 2nd story				Frame sweep			
2nd story exterior walls stood				Rough alarm wire			
2nd story interior walls stood				Rough vacuum plumbing			
Tubs/showers set				FRAME INSPECTION			
Plumb & line				VA FRAME INSPECTION			
Trusses delivered				Measure for cabinets			
Trusses installed				Drain/waste/overflow drained			
Order HVAC ducts				Re-cover tubs/showers			
Rafters installed				Wall insulation			
Roof sheathing				INSULATION INSPECTION			
Phone interface/cable box				Order interior doors			
Notify plumbers—start				Furnaces ordered			
Shear installed				Temporary heat for drywall			
ROOF/SHEAR NAIL INSPECTION				Schedule garage doors			
Scaffolding single story				Studs straightened			
Windows installed				Drywall hung			
Siding installed				DRYWALL NAIL INSPECTION			

Project Log and Checklists (page 5 of 6)

Plan/Elevation _____ Lot # _____

	SCHD Today's Date	SCHD for	Work Complete		SCHD Today's Date	SCH D for	Work Complete
GAS LINE PRESSURE INSPECTION				Schedule leaded/etched glass			
Gas meter installed				Pick & rake—graders			
Sheetrock textured				Finish grading			
Walk-through notification—sales				Fencing			
Pipe/sleeves—flatwork				Wrought iron			
Sewer boxes—driveways				Landscaping			
Fireplace faces				Heat for vinyl			
Plastering				Lino scrape			
Downspouts installed				Particle board installed			
STUCCO INSPECTION				Vinyl installed			
Exterior paint				Hardwood floors installed			
Scaffolds down				Base over vinyl/second trim			
Pick & rake flat concrete				Finish hardware			
Flat concrete poured				Bar stools installed			
Order condensing units				Closet shelves installed			
Cabinets delivered				Cabinets adjusted			
Order 1x4/plywood cabinet decking				Plumbing trim			
Kitchen sinks ordered				Appliances installed			
Interior trim				Carpet sweep			
Handrails installed				Carpet installation			
Interior paint				Window coverings installed			
Hardware delivered				Detail house			
Lights delivered				Screens installed			
Order appliances				Fireplace doors installed			
Roofers—lay tile				Gas fireplaces started up			
Cabinets installed				Sidewalks repaired			
Measure for countertops				HVAC start-up/clean furnace filter			
Tile/marble installed				HOUSE FINAL			
Extra tile				VA HOUSE FINAL			
Vanity tops				Paint touch-up			
Shower enclosures/mirrors				Final clean			
HVAC trim				Tub repair			
Formica installed				Silicon showers/tubs			
Electric trim				Garages cleaned			
Finish trim				Finish vacuum			
Windows/tubs cleaned				Garage cabinets installed			
Paint fireplaces/bumper pipe/CAR				Pressure wash concrete			
Schedule screens/fireplace doors				Walk-through			

General Notes (page 6 of 6)

Project Log and Checklists (page 1 of 6)

Parcel # _____   Address _____   Lot # _____

Project #_____   Unit # _____   Phase # _____

Plan # _____   Elevation _____   Permit # _____

When a house is released to build: order, check, schedule

____ Portable latrines _____

____ Permit #s vs. lot #s vs. address #s _____

____ Plot maps _____

____ Are there storm drains in driveways? _____

____ Sequence sheets _____

____ Locate & mark property pins _____

____ Locate & mark utilities _____

____ Order bumper pipe for garage slabs _____

____ Order mudsill (sleepers) for foundations _____

____ Temporary power pole _____

____ Wash out area for concrete trucks _____

____ Retaining walls _____

____ Steel beams _____

____ Roof materials _____

____ Steel columns _____

____ Trusses _____

____ Exterior doors & pocket door frames _____

____ Windows _____

____ Attic & gable vents _____

____ Termite flashing _____

____ Interior & exterior lights _____

____ Exterior hardware _____

____ Insulation for framers, plumbers, and lathers _____

____ Drywall for framers _____

____ Trash bins set up _____

____ Location from Post Office where mailbox units go __

____ A.D.A. requirements _____

Daily/Weekly Reminders

____ Call-in time _____

____ Safety meetings _____

____ Progress reports _____

____ SWPPP reports _____

____ Walk models _____

____ Change model flags _____

____ Clean dirt & mud from gutters and storm drains ____

____ Mark electrical panels _____

____ Mark windows _____

____ Order fireplace chase pans _____

____ Order tubs/showers for framers _____

____ Temporary guard/handrails _____

____ Order windows _____

____ Order exterior doors & pocket door frames _____

____ Cover thresholds _____

____ Line sets (freon) _____

____ Cover tubs and showers _____

____ Garage door keys/temporary locks _____

____ Order appliances _____

____ Heat for vinyl/drywall _____

____ Pipe/sleeves for flatwork _____

____ Sewer cleanout boxes _____

____ Retaining walls _____

____ Mailbox pads _____

____ Notify Post Office to set mailbox units _____

____ Lights delivered _____

____ Hardware delivered _____

____ Wrought iron _____

____ Handrails _____

____ Leaded/etched glass _____

____ Condensing units _____

____ Hackouts/broken windows replaced _____

____ Paint fireplaces/bumper pipes/cold air returns _____

____ Floor squeaks fixed before carpet _____

____ Concrete patched before carpet _____

____ Roof gutters cleaned _____

____ Utility companies—final trim _____

____ Sidewalks repaired _____

____ HVAC start-ups _____

____ Return portable latrines _____

Project Log and Checklists (page 2 of 6)

Lot # _____   **Address** _____   **Plan/Elevation** _____

Options	Yes	No	Subs Notified	Extras	Yes	No	Subs Notified
Change orders received				Change orders received			
Bedroom/den/retreat				Concrete			
Fireplaces				Backyard landscaping			
2-car garage				Vacuum			
3-car garage				Plumbing			
Sewing room/shop				Electrical			
Ceiling fans				HVAC			
Bedroom lights				Alarm			
Kitchen tile				Garage door opener			
Entry tile				Window coverings			
Opaque glass				R.V. gate (extra wide)			
Microwave oven				Speaker wire			
Finish garage				Interior wall insulation			
Hardwood floors				Wallpaper			
Skylights				Gas log lighter			
Decks				Drywall bullnose corners			
Other:				Other:			

Project Log and Checklists (page 3 of 6)

Plan/Elevation _____   Lot # _____

From Homeowners, Sales Representatives, Office:		SCHD Today's Date	SCHD for	Work Complete
Siding type	Layout/chalk			
Brick type	Trench/excavate			
Stone type	FOOTING INSPECTION			
Stucco type	Forms set			
Garage door style	Sleeves/conduit			
Fireplace model #	Electrical panels			
Roof type /number	Footings poured			
Cabinet colors	STEM WALL INSPECTION			
Paint colors (interior)	Stem walls poured			
	Ground plumbing			
	Plumbing extras			
	GROUND PLUMBING/SETBACK INSPECTION			
Paint colors (exterior)	Termite spray			
	Mechanical extras			
	FOUNDATION INSPECTION			
	VA FOUNDATION INSPECTION			
	Slump/cylinder/saturation tests			
	Slab poured			
Formica selections	GARAGE SLAB INSPECTION			
Tile selections	Bumper pipes installed			
Vinyl selections	Garage slump/cylinder tests			
Carpet selections	Garage slab poured			
Pad size	Foundation waterproofed			
Appliance type	Window wells installed			
Appliance color	Foundation backfilled			
Gutter type	"As Builts" foundation			
Fence type	"As Builts" plumbing			
	TEMPORARY POWER INSPECTION			
	Utility trenches dug/barricaded			
	Trenches backfilled			
	Plumbing trench dug/barricaded			
	SEWER & WATER INSPECTION			
	Plumbing trench backfilled			
	Trenches jetted			
	Electric, phone, cable, gas			
	Plumbing			
	Schedule exterior door delivery			
	Schedule tubs/showers			

Project Log and Checklists (page 4 of 6)

Plan/Elevation _____ Lot # _____

	SCHD Today's Date	SCHD for	Work Complete		SCHD Today's Date	SCH D for	Work Complete
Schedule steel				Framing pick-up			
Framing material drop				Rough plumbing			
Layout/snap lines				Plumbing extras			
Plate				HVAC—gutters/flashing			
Girders/joists installed				Line sets—freon			
Subfloor plumbing				Fireplaces installed			
Subfloor HVAC—ducts				FIREPLACES INSPECTED			
Subfloor electrical				Felt & batt roof			
SUBFLOOR FRAME INSPECTION				Composition/shake roof installed			
Subfloor insulation				Lots scrapped			
SUBFLOOR INSULATION INSPECTION				Tubs/showers covered			
Subfloor decking				Rough HVAC—ducts			
Schedule window installation				Masonry—veneers			
Schedule fireplace installation				Insulate tubs/shear/soffits			
Schedule fireplace chase pans				Flashing for lathers			
Exterior walls framed/stood				Lathers			
Interior walls framed/stood				Hot mop			
Tubs/showers set				Stock sheetrock			
Plumb & line				Stock roof tile			
Electric meters set				Rough electric			
2nd story floor joists				Electrical extras			
Scaffold ordered 2nd story				Frame sweep			
2nd story exterior walls stood				Rough alarm wire			
2nd story interior walls stood				Rough vacuum plumbing			
Tubs/showers set				FRAME INSPECTION			
Plumb & line				VA FRAME INSPECTION			
Trusses delivered				Measure for cabinets			
Trusses installed				Drain/waste/overflow drained			
Order HVAC ducts				Re-cover tubs/showers			
Rafters installed				Wall insulation			
Roof sheathing				INSULATION INSPECTION			
Phone interface/cable box				Order interior doors			
Notify plumbers—start				Furnaces ordered			
Shear installed				Temporary heat for drywall			
ROOF/SHEAR NAIL INSPECTION				Schedule garage doors			
Scaffolding single story				Studs straightened			
Windows installed				Drywall hung			
Siding installed				DRYWALL NAIL INSPECTION			

Project Log and Checklists (page 5 of 6)

Plan/Elevation _____ Lot # _____

	SCHD Today's Date	SCHD for	Work Complete		SCHD Today's Date	SCHD for	Work Complete
GAS LINE PRESSURE INSPECTION				Schedule leaded/etched glass			
Gas meter installed				Pick & rake—graders			
Sheetrock textured				Finish grading			
Walk-through notification—sales				Fencing			
Pipe/sleeves—flatwork				Wrought iron			
Sewer boxes—driveways				Landscaping			
Fireplace faces				Heat for vinyl			
Plastering				Lino scrape			
Downspouts installed				Particle board installed			
STUCCO INSPECTION				Vinyl installed			
Exterior paint				Hardwood floors installed			
Scaffolds down				Base over vinyl/second trim			
Pick & rake flat concrete				Finish hardware			
Flat concrete poured				Bar stools installed			
Order condensing units				Closet shelves installed			
Cabinets delivered				Cabinets adjusted			
Order 1x4/plywood cabinet decking				Plumbing trim			
Kitchen sinks ordered				Appliances installed			
Interior trim				Carpet sweep			
Handrails installed				Carpet installation			
Interior paint				Window coverings installed			
Hardware delivered				Detail house			
Lights delivered				Screens installed			
Order appliances				Fireplace doors installed			
Roofers—lay tile				Gas fireplaces started up			
Cabinets installed				Sidewalks repaired			
Measure for countertops				HVAC start-up/clean furnace filter			
Tile/marble installed				HOUSE FINAL			
Extra tile				VA HOUSE FINAL			
Vanity tops				Paint touch-up			
Shower enclosures/mirrors				Final clean			
HVAC trim				Tub repair			
Formica installed				Silicon showers/tubs			
Electric trim				Garages cleaned			
Finish trim				Finish vacuum			
Windows/tubs cleaned				Garage cabinets installed			
Paint fireplaces/bumper pipe/CAR				Pressure wash concrete			
Schedule screens/fireplace doors				Walk-through			

General Notes (page 6 of 6)